THE LOCKLEY-PETERSON GUIDE TO THE
FOSSIL FOOTPRINTS
OF THE WORLD

Text and Photographs by Martin Lockley
Illustrations by Judy Peterson

DEDICATION – To Pliny Moody
the Massachusetts farm boy
who found the first
dinosaur tracks in 1802.
Never knowing what he started,
he has helped all in our field
to celebrate 200 years
of tracking ancient life.
1802-2002

ISBN 0-9706091-3-2

©2002

A Lockley-Peterson publication
produced and distributed in conjunction with
the University of Colorado at Denver, Dinosaur Trackers
and The Friends of Dinosaur Ridge, Morrison, Colorado.
Partial proceeds go to dinosaur tracks research.

www.dinoridge.org

CONTENTS

WHAT THIS BOOK IS ABOUT

Have you ever wondered what the tracks of *T. rex* look like? Are the footprints shown in the movie Jurassic Park accurate? Did you know that fossil footprints have their own special scientific names?

This little book is a handy guide to most of what we know about fossil footprints from around the world. It covers the main track types, and probable trackmakers from the best known groups of amphibians, pre-dinosaurian reptiles, dinosaurs, pterosaurs and extinct mammals such as mammoths, cave bears and our human ancestors.

Tracking extinct animals is the ultimate detective work. Finding the foot that fits the footprint reminds us of the search for Cinderella. Some tracks can be matched with the animals that made them, while the tracks of some well-known species remain completely unknown. Yet others were made by creatures not yet known from skeletons.

Join us in tracking through this lost world of prehistoric footprints and discover clues as to where and how extinct creatures went about their daily lives.

INTRODUCTION
What We Can learn From Fossil Footprints

Fossil footprints must have been known to ancient peoples for thousands of years, and were probably a source of amazement. How can footprints be preserved in solid rock, and yet often look as fresh as if they were made just yesterday? The modern study of footprints by paleontologists dates back less than two hundred years. During this time, however, many advances in the study of fossil footprints have been made, and this area of research is now considered an important area within the study of paleontology as a whole.

So what types of footprints are preserved and what can we learn from them? It is perhaps surprising that the fossilized tracks and traces of a large number of different types of animals are much more common than we might expect. Not only do we find abundant remains of tracks of large animals such as dinosaurs, ancient rhinos, etc., but we also find the delicate

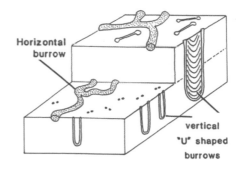

Trace fossils

traces of tiny mammals, spiders and other invertebrates. Many invertebrates, that is, animals without backbones (such as clams, snails, sea urchins

Paleontologists and volunteers in the field

and worms) do not have proper legs so they do not leave footprints. However they may make burrows or crawling trails, what geologists and paleontologists call trace fossils.

Mostly, however, we hear about the trace fossils of vertebrates (animals with backbones) which belong to the familiar classes known as amphibians, reptiles, birds and mammals. These animals are sometimes called tetrapods (meaning four legs), which distinguish them from the only other important group of vertebrates well-known to us as fish. Fish sometimes leave winding, sinuous trails when touching the bottom sediment as they swim.

The fossil record, however, contains the footprints of many species of extinct animals that are quite different from the familiar amphibians, reptiles, birds and mammals still living today. Among the best known examples are the tracks and trackways of dinosaurs, pterosaurs, and mammal-like reptiles such as Dimetrodon. We shall explore these and more in this book.

It is precisely because dinosaurs and other animals are extinct that we find their tracks or trace fossils so useful in paleontological studies. In fact there are some animals known only from their tracks. In other words, no actual fossil skeletons, also called body fossils, exist to tell us what the trackmaker looked like. One can imagine then how useful the tracks are in telling us something about creatures that would otherwise remain com-

pletely unknown. For example, the famous nineteenth century paleontologist Edward Hitchcock from Massachusetts studied 200 million-year-old

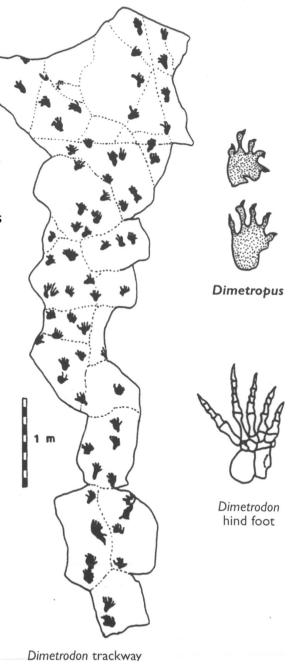

Dimetropus

Dimetrodon
hind foot

Dimetrodon trackway

3

Trampling of plants and clams

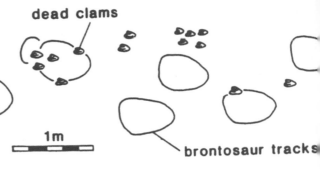

dead clams

1m

brontosaur tracks

Jurassic dinosaur tracks found in 1802, long before any dinosaurs were known in North America, and before any were known from the Early Jurassic. This created a tricky Sherlock Holmes mystery, making it very hard for Hitchcock to figure out "who dun it."

A lot of facts can be gleaned from tracks if we study them carefully. They tell us how big animals were and how many toes they had on their feet. This is very useful in helping to identify them. Footprints also tell us which way animals were going, and how many there were in any given area. Sometimes we find skin impressions preserved. This is particularly helpful for reconstruct-

ing animals, since skin is rarely found preserved with skeletons. Trackways also reveal length of step and stride and whether an animal was walking or hopping. They tell us whether it was sprawling and cumbersome, or walking upright and erect. Some-

Ceratopsian and hind footprint

times tracks also provide evidence that dinosaurs and other ancient animals traveled in large herds, or that they were responsible for trampling other plants and animals underfoot.

Iguanodon and hind footprint

4

DETECTIVE WORK
How To Track Extinct Animals

In any kind of detective work, the first thing one needs is good information. This means collecting measurements, photographs and notes on your observations. Usually with footprints, we measure the size of the track and the length of the step, where it is found, and the type of rock in which it is preserved. In addition one can make tracings on transparent paper or plastic film. Clear acetate film or transparent plastic works well.

Making tracings allows you to spend a little time going over the shape of the footprint, and getting to know it. One can trace several footprints in a series (trackway) and see if they are consistently similar, as they should be, or if they differ because some are better preserved than others. We can then reduce our tracings to an appropriate size on a photocopy machine or computer, and produce our final diagram showing the important features.

We can now see the size and shape of footprints clearly, and record the number of toe or digit impressions and the angles between them, the step length, the angle between steps, and the width or straddle of the trackway.

Track shapes and numbered toes

Three -toed tracks

NO TOES

Four-toed tracks

NO TOES

Five-toed track

5

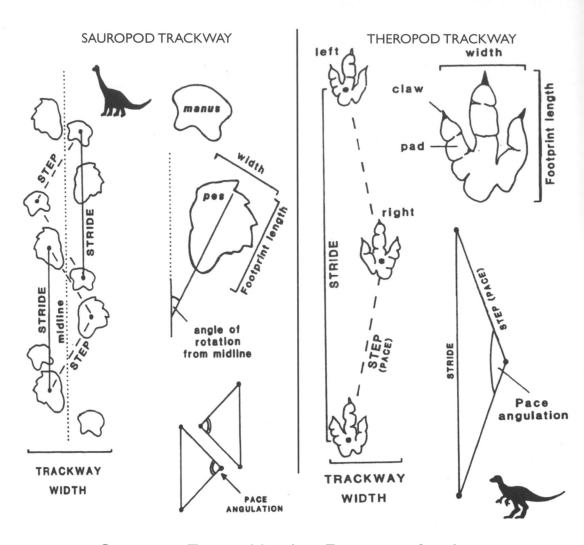

SAUROPOD TRACKWAY

manus

pes

width

Footprint length

angle of
rotation
from midline

STEP

STRIDE

STRIDE

midline

STEP

STRIDE

TRACKWAY
WIDTH

PACE
ANGULATION

THEROPOD TRACKWAY

left

claw

pad

right

width

Footprint length

STRIDE

STEP
(PACE)

STRIDE

STEP (PACE)

Pace
angulation

TRACKWAY
WIDTH

Common Terms Used in Footprint Studies

Footprint or track: means a single footprint.

Trackway: means a series of footprints or track made by a single animal.

Trail: has several meanings, either a continuous path, like a game trail, made by many animals, or a continuous mark made by a crawling animal such as a worm or snail. Sometimes people use track and trail with the same meaning as trackway.

Digit impressions: Trackers count digits from 1 to 5 using Roman numerals (I,II,III,IV,V). Start with the inside, equivalent to our thumb or big toe and count out to the little toe or finger. The big toe, or digit I, is sometimes called the hallux in birds and dinosaurs. Only very few abnormal animals have more than five digits and many have fewer. We use the terms monodactyl (1), didactyl (2), tridactyl (3), tetradactyl (4) and pentadactyl (5) to describe feet according to the number of digits. You should easily be able to tell in which category a track belongs. Polydactyl means having more than the normal number of digits (six or more), and is usually a freak of nature.

Digit angles: the different angles between toe impressions.

Orientation: direction in which track or trackway is heading.

Step or Pace: a single step from left foot to right, or from right to left.

Stride: two steps, from left to next left, or from right to next right.

Pace angle: (or pace angulation) angle made between three successive footprints.

Straddle or trackway width: the widest point of the trackway.

Tail traces: some trackways, especially those of long- bodied, short-legged creatures like salamanders or lizards show tail traces. However, in general tail traces are rare, especially for dinosaurs and mammals.

Heel, ankle, pelvis, skin and body impressions: sometimes dinosaurs and other animals crouched down leaving heel, ankle or pelvis impressions. Rarely an animal in crouching position may leave impressions of other parts of the body including its skin texture pattern. Skin impressions are also sometimes found in clear footprints.

Plantigrade: means flat-footed or walking on the plantar surface of the foot.

Digitigrade: means walking on tip toes or the tips of the digits.

Ichnology: from the Greek word *ichnos* meaning trace, is the study of all tracks and trace fossils.

Paleontology: meaning "the study of ancient beings" is a necessary area of knowledge for those who study ancient fossil footprints.

Finding Footprints

It is easy to find modern footprints along beaches and lake shores. This allows the keen tracker the opportunity to practice their tracking skills by recording what they find. Many field guides are available to help us identify the tracks of birds, mammals and other species. The keen tracker can easily learn to make track replicas by pouring plaster of Paris into the track.

One should then remember to record where the track came from, what type of animal made it and other details such as direction of travel.

However, tracking extinct animals is a different type of science. When tracking extinct animals we must know the age and type of rock in which footprints are found. If the track is important to preserve for scientific study, it may be taken to a museum. However, often paleontologists make a replica by painting on a rubber mold compound such as silicon latex. Once this has dried, it can then be used to make replicas from Plaster of Paris or

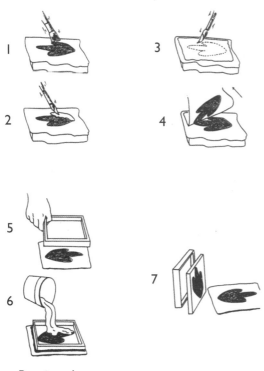

Pouring plaster

fiberglass. This is not easy to do without experience, so consult a paleontologist or expert in the field. Fossil tracks cannot be replicated properly by pouring plaster on the rock. Do not do this! The plaster usually sticks to the rock like cement and is impossible to get off. Last, but not least, never study, replicate or collect a fossil footprint without the permission

of the landowner. Permits are almost always required before working on public land.

Be professional and keep track of the location of sites where tracks are found. Each location or site can be called a tracksite. Sometimes many different tracksites form part of a large layer of strata in which tracks are very abundant. Paleontologists have named these track-rich layers "dinosaur freeways" or megatracksites. They show that in some areas animals such as dinosaurs made literally millions of tracks over large areas. The term "mega" refers to the size of the site and not the size of the tracks. Such freeways suggest that animals moved back and forth over large areas, possibly in migrating herds. Some megatracksites cover tens of thousands of square miles. Here then are three more terms:

Tracksite: a site where one finds tracks.

Megatracksite: a single layer or geological stratum in which we find many tracks over a huge area. If the tracks are those of dinosaurs we can also call them dinosaur freeways, but megatracksites may also contain the tracks of many different types of animals.

Dinosaur Freeway: has the same meaning as dinosaur megatracksite.

FOOTPRINT FACTS
The Smallest and Largest Tracks; the Longest Trackways

The smallest footprints
The smallest footprints we are likely to find are probably those of arthropods, such as millipedes or insects. These can be about a millimeter in diameter so that we can find as many as 25 on each side of an inch-long trail. Look for such tracks around mud puddles as they dry up a day or two after a rainfall. Such footprints have been found in 450 million-year-old rocks in England, and may represent some of the first millipede-like animals to walk on land.

The smallest vertebrate footprints
The smallest tracks of vertebrates are typically those of small rodents such as mice and shrews. The oldest known mammal tracks, for example, are less than half an inch long, and they come from rocks that are more than 200 million years old. Tracks of small birds, such as sparrows, are also very small, as are the tracks of small reptiles such as lizards. Of course the tracks of baby animals are always smaller than those of adults.

Mother and baby Iguanodonts

© J. Peterson '99

Although most dinosaur tracks were quite large, or even gigantic, some are very small. Some species of dinosaurs never grew larger than pigeons or turkeys, even as adults, so their tracks are only an inch or two in length. Tracks of baby dinosaurs, however, are very rare, and there are not many good examples of footprints that are proven to be those of babies. One problem with finding the tracks of babies is that they may have stayed in their nests until they were already partially grown. Even if they did move out early, they were too small and light to leave many clear tracks.

The largest footprints
The largest fossil footprints are those of sauropods or brontosaurs. The hind foot, or pes, can be about 1 meter (or

40 inches) in diameter, and some reports suggest a diameter of as much as 1.1 or 1.2 meters (44-48 inches). This is about twice the diameter of a large elephant footprint. The largest three-toed track, made by *Tyrannosaurus rex,* is 85 cm (34 inches) long. Some tracks appear a little longer than they really are because the heel dragged behind the foot.

The longest trackways
The longest trackway in the world, that is, the longest continuously measured series of left and right footprints of a single animal, is 311 meters (1020 feet). This trackway (name *Megalosauripus*), made by a carnivorous dinosaur, was reported from 150 million-year-old late Jurassic strata in Turkmenistan, in central Asia. Some individual tracks from this site are 75 cm long (30 inches), which makes them the largest tracks of carnivorous dinosaurs known from the Jurassic. The previous world record was a 147 meter (482 feet) sauropod trackway from 175 million-year-old middle Jurassic strata in Portugal.

The largest trackside in the world where one can follow a single surface covered with footprints is probably a site near Sucre in Bolivia. Here one can see 65-70 million-year-old Cretaceous dinosaur tracks covering a nearly vertical limestone cliff face that is 200 feet high and 3/4 mile long. In order to study this site, researchers had to rappel down the face on ropes (see pages 74-75).

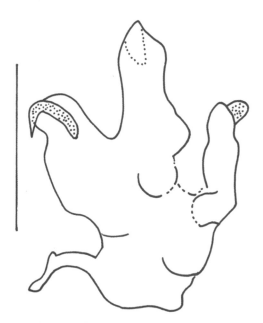

Tyrannosaurus rex probably made the largest known three-toed track. Scale 50 cm

The world's largest track of a carnivorous dinosaur.
Made by *Tyrannosaurus*. Track name: **Tyrannosauripus**

12   Another very large and deep track made by a Sauropod. Late Jurassic. Colorado.

MODERN RESEARCH
on Fossil Footprints: Good and Bad Ideas

Dinosaur speed

We already know that fossil footprints are useful for understanding the behavior of extinct animals. They also allow us to estimate the speed of dinosaurs and other animals. Calculations suggest that the fastest dinosaur was a medium-sized theropod that was moving at about 25 miles per hour (40 km), which is about the speed necessary to win the 100-meter dash in the Olympics. This trackway of a speedy dinosaur comes from 110 million-year-old Cretaceous strata in Texas.

Most other trackways of running dinosaurs seem to have also been made by theropods. Most of the trackways of large dinosaurs, such as brontosaurs, armored dinosaurs, and horned dinosaurs, show that they moved quite slowly. This is to be expected given their great size. One trackway of an armored dinosaur from Bolivia suggests that it was running at a modest speed of about 7 miles per hour (11 km per hour).

Sprawling and tail dragging

We used to think that dinosaurs and other primitive prehistoric animals were very clumsy and cumbersome. They used to be depicted with their feet widely splayed apart and their tails dragging. Trackways of most dinosaurs show that they did not drag their tails. Their trackways are also quite narrow, suggesting that they walked upright and did not sprawl. In fact a modern lizard sprawls and drags its tail more than an ancient dinosaur.

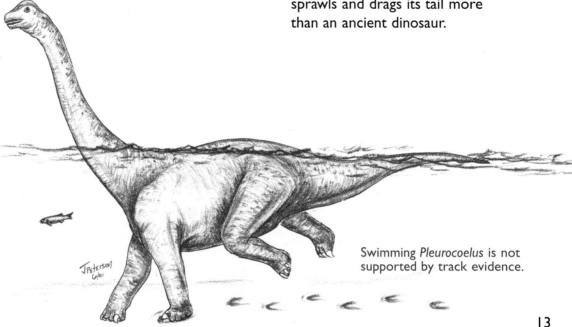

Swimming *Pleurocoelus* is not supported by track evidence.

Walking *Pleurocoelus* is supported by track evidence

Swimming and hopping dinosaurs and mammals?

Some brontosaur trackways show only the impressions of the front feet. This might suggest that the animals were swimming along touching the bottom with their front feet. This rather bad idea has been disproved by the finding that the front feet sank in deeper than the back feet. This causes the front feet to leave impressions on layers beneath the surface. Paleontologists call these *undertracks* or *underprints*.

There have been a few reports of hopping dinosaurs. Although it is exciting to think of a hopping dinosaur, unfortunately the evidence is not convincing. In one case the tracks turned out to be those of a swimming turtle touching the bottom with both flippers at the same time.

There are reliable reports of hopping mammals from 175-200 million-year-old Jurassic strata in South America. These animals however, were very small and probably resembled gerbils or kangaroo mice. There are also reports of trackways made by hopping frogs and song birds. It seems that with the exception of kangaroos and rock hopper penguins, it is mainly small animals that hop, and not big dinosaurs.

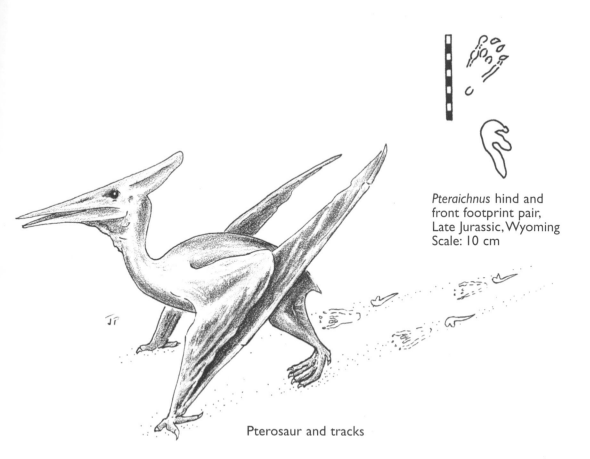

Pteraichnus hind and front footprint pair, Late Jurassic, Wyoming
Scale: 10 cm

Pterosaur and tracks

Pterosaurs or crocodiles?

There has been quite a debate about what pterosaur tracks look like. Some people have suggested that pterosaurs walked on their hind legs like birds, while others have suggested that they walked on all fours, using the knuckles of their wing limbs. The tracks prove that they walked this way. The three fingers on the wrist have a very distinctive shape that shows up well in tracks. Generally pterosaurs had very small hind legs in comparison with their large wings, so it is not surprising that they leaned forward onto their wrists.

In the past not everyone agreed that pterosaurs walked on all fours – and some people thought that their trackways were made by crocodiles. As we could not study the footprints of live pterosaurs, we did not know what to expect. However, enough trackways have been found that now we do know what they look like. Pterosaurs had skinny tails or no tails at all, and so no tail traces. Crocodiles, however, have long heavy tails that leave obvious marks. Most paleontologists now know the difference between the tracks of these animals.

Trampling of clams

Social dinosaurs

We used to think that dinosaurs were solitary creatures, like most living reptiles. We now know that many groups, especially the brontosaurs, the duckbills and the horned dinosaurs were social and traveled in herds. Sites where we find dozens of trackways heading in the same direction prove this point. There is now no doubt that some dinosaurs traveled in herds.

Trampling

Imagine the damage done by a herd of 100 brontosaurs, or perhaps even a herd of a thousand or more. In recent years paleontologists have found sites where there was extensive trampling of the soils and sediments of lake shores and river banks. This trampling also flattened many plants and killed off small creatures such as clams and snails that could not get out of the way. Even animals that can move are in danger of being trampled and killed by large herds. Today in Africa we can find dead frogs, lizards and other animals left behind after large herds pass by. Some trails made by hippos are as wide as roads and become new channels for rivers when floods spill into these heavily trampled routes.

Geologic Time Scale

Era	Period	Epoch	Million Yrs
CENOZOIC	QUATERNARY	Holocene	0
CENOZOIC	QUATERNARY	Pleistocene	1
CENOZOIC	TERTIARY	Pliocene	2 / 5
CENOZOIC	TERTIARY	Miocene	23
CENOZOIC	TERTIARY	Oligocene	35
CENOZOIC	TERTIARY	Eocene	56
CENOZOIC	TERTIARY	Paleocene	66
MESOZOIC	CRETACEOUS	Late	
MESOZOIC	CRETACEOUS	Early	145
MESOZOIC	JURASSIC	Late	
MESOZOIC	JURASSIC	Middle	
MESOZOIC	JURASSIC	Early	208
MESOZOIC	TRIASSIC	Late	
MESOZOIC	TRIASSIC	Middle	
MESOZOIC	TRIASSIC	Early	245
UPPER PALEOZOIC	PERMIAN	Late	
UPPER PALEOZOIC	PERMIAN	Early	290
UPPER PALEOZOIC	CARBONIFEROUS	Late	323
UPPER PALEOZOIC	CARBONIFEROUS	Early	363
UPPER PALEOZOIC	DEVONIAN		410
LOWER PALEOZOIC	SILURIAN		440
LOWER PALEOZOIC	ORDOVICIAN		495
LOWER PALEOZOIC	CAMBRIAN		545

THE AGE OF FOSSIL FOOTPRINTS

Paleontologists study the history of life on earth as if it were a series of chapters in a book. For these reasons it is important to keep track of who was around in the different geological time periods. When we follow the evolution of animals through time we see that each time period had its own distinctive cast of characters. We can follow this history through the track record as well as through the record of bones.

From fish to reptiles

Fossil footprints of marine trilobites date back more than 500 million years to the Cambrian Period. The first millipedes to walk on land are almost as old, and date from the Ordovician Period at about 450 million years ago. The first vertebrates to leave tracks were amphibians that looked like fish with stumpy legs instead of fins. At first they may have walked on the bottom of lakes, and not on land. Their tracks date from the **Devonian Period** almost 400 million years ago, but they are very rare.

Left: Geologic Time Scale

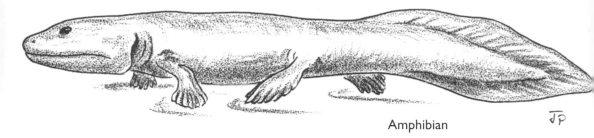

Amphibian JP

The **Carboniferous Period**, beginning about 350 million years ago, is known as the Age of Amphibians and coal swamps. Tracks became more common at this time, and the wet conditions lead to many being preserved. Many were made by amphibians; others are lizard-like, though they were not made by true lizards.

The next period, the **Permian**, began about 280 million years ago, and is sometimes known as the Age of Reptiles. Many tracks from this time period were made by mammal-like reptiles, or proto-mammals, that are distantly related to true mammals such as ourselves. The fin-backed reptile *Dimetrodon* is one of the earliest of this group. It had tracks that were quite similar to those of modern dogs and cats. They remind us of just how far back we can trace the family tree of mammals.

The Age of Dinosaurs
The **Triassic**, beginning about 250 million years ago, marks the beginning of the Age of Dinosaurs, though the first dinosaur did not appear or leave tracks until around 220 million years ago. It was a small animal with chicken-sized feet. It was not until the **Jurassic,** beginning around 200 million years ago, that dinosaurs became abundant. Mostly the tracks are those of the lizard-hipped dinosaurs (saurischians), especially the theropods and the brontosaurs. In the Late Jurassic we also find lots of small pterosaur tracks.

During the **Cretaceous**, beginning about 145 million years ago, we find lots of tracks of bird-hipped dinosaurs (Ornithischians), especially the duck-billed dinosaurs (Iguanodontids and Hadrosaurids). We also find the trackways of armored and horned dinosaurs (ankylosaurs and ceratopsians). Pterosaur tracks in the Cretaceous are generally much larger than those in the Jurassic, but are less common. However we find many tracks of the first birds.

The Age of Mammals

Beginning about 65 million years ago, after the extinction of the dinosaurs and pterosaurs, we come to the Age of Mammals, known as the **Tertiary Period**. In the early days mammals were small and sparse. The few tracks that were found were made mainly by odd-toed hoofed mammals (ungulates) such as the tapir and the ancestor to the horse. We also find quite a few bird tracks. Later in the Age of Mammals we find that even-toed or "cloven-hoofed" mammal tracks are more common such as those made by the ancestors of sheep, cattle, deer, camels, pigs and so forth. Late in the Tertiary we find the first tracks of our hominid ancestors. These include the world-famous 3.5 million-year-old tracks of *Australopithecus*

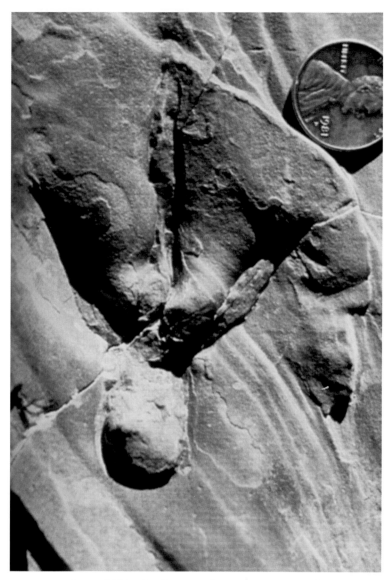

A small Triassic dinosaur footprint preserved as a natural impression. Colorado.

from Tanzania.

Finally we come to the **Quaternary Period**, the last one-and-a-half to two million years. This was what we popularly know as the Ice Age, which ended only 10-12,000 years ago. During this time period we find the tracks of mammoth, cave lion, cave bear and reindeer, all animals that would have been familiar to our cave-dwelling ancestors.

In 1969 humans made tracks on the moon for the first time. It is interesting to imagine what paleontologists from the future might think if they were to find the footprints of astronaut boots in the moon dust, and how they might interpret them.

A large Jurassic dinosaur footprint as it was found in the field, preserved as a natural cast. Entrada Formation, Utah.

FAMOUS TRACKERS

The modern sciences of geology and paleontology began about 200 years ago. At that time scientists studying natural history began to stop calling fossils "natural curiosities" and began to realize that they represented evidence of ancient life on planet Earth. It was at this time that natural scientists began to pay serious attention to fossils as useful for scientific study.

Reverend William Buckland, Oxford, England (1820s-1830s). The first paleontologist to take a serious interest in fossil footprints was the Reverend William Buckland, who was the first professor of geology at Oxford University, beginning around 1820. In the late 1820s fossil footprints from Permian sandstones in Scotland were reported to Buckland and he suggested that they were probably made by a tortoise. He is alleged to have woken his wife in the middle of the night to get her to make pastry dough, on which he set his pet tortoise. It made tracks very similar to those from the ancient rocks in Scotland, which we

Permian tracks named *Laoporus* from Scotland were the first fossil footprints ever reported in the scientific

literature. William Buckland first attributed them to a tortoise. They are now known to be those of mammal-like reptiles.

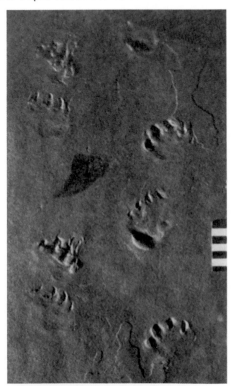

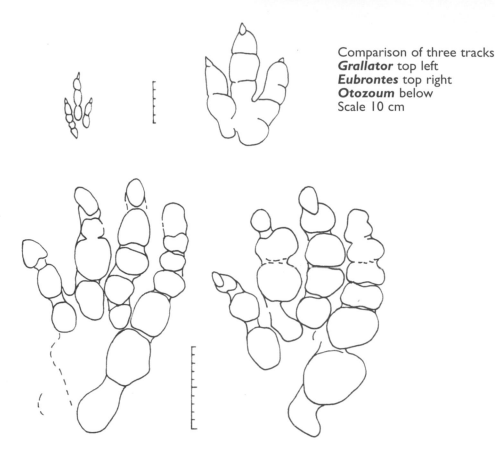

Comparison of three tracks
Grallator top left
Eubrontes top right
Otozoum below
Scale 10 cm

now know to be more than 250 million years old, from before the Age of Dinosaurs. We now attribute these tracks to mammal-like reptiles, but they are still named **Chelichnus**, meaning like a tortoise or turtle track.

Buckland's tracks in the pastry dough experiment became so famous that he repeated it many times for students and distinguished scientific visitors, often converting skeptics to the idea that fossil footprints were very important. Buckland was also famous for inventing the study of fossil feces or "coprolites," and for doing experiments on how hyenas chew bones. This was important because, at that time, many caves were found full of hyena droppings and chewed remains of marrow

bones. Buckland proved, with tracks and bones, that many animals that are now extinct or no longer living in England had been common in ancient times.

Reverend Edward Hitchcock, Amherst, Massachusetts (1830s-1860s). Reverend Edward Hitchcock is remembered, even more than Buckland, for devoting a career of thirty years to the study of bird-like Jurassic tracks from New England, most of which we now know were made by dinosaurs. In fact Hitchcock has been described as the father of fossil footprint studies (known as vertebrate ichnology). When he began his work in the 1830s the concept of dinosaurs did not exist, and so he believed, like everyone else, that the small and large three-toed tracks were made by birds. In jest, many were called the tracks of "Noah's Raven" or the footprints of very heavy poultry that could leave indentations in rock!

The most famous Jurassic tracks named by Hitchcock, and now well-known around the world, were *Grallator*, a raven-sized track, and the much larger *Eubrontes*, more than a foot long. Both were three-toed and had at first been named *Ornithoichnities*, meaning stony bird track — the first scientific Latin name ever given to a fossil footprint. Hitchcock also found some large four-toed tracks that he knew had not been made by birds; he named these *Otozoum*. He interpreted these and other tracks as those of various reptiles, amphibians and primitive mammals. He also described the tracks and trails of insects, beetles and other small arthropods.

Sir Arthur Conan Doyle, (1910s-1920s). Sir Arthur Conan Doyle, the famous creator of the super sleuth detective Sherlock Holmes, had quite an interest in dinosaur tracks that were commonly found near his home in Sussex, England. He was the first author to write a popular and very famous science fiction book about dinosaurs. In this exciting story, entitled *The Lost World,* intrepid explorers had many adventures following and interpreting *Iguanodon* dinosaur tracks.

Roland T. Bird, American Museum, New York (1930s-1940s). Although Roland T. Bird, or "R.T." as he was affectionately known, worked for the American Museum of Natural History in New York, he is most famous for his study of tracks in the western USA, especially in Texas, where he found the first well-authenticated brontosaur tracks. When he excavated the site, along the Paluxy River, at what is now Dinosaur Valley State Park, he found trackways of carnivorous dinosaurs running parallel to those of the brontosaurs. This gave rise to the controversial interpretation that one of the carnivores had attacked one of the brontosaurs. This interpretation is still debated today.

Bird mounted a massive excavation of segments of the parallel carnivore and brontosaur trackways and in 1944, during the war, shipped his precious cargo to New York. As a result he worried during the whole journey that the shipment might be sunk by a German U-boat and end up at the bottom of the Atlantic Ocean. Bird also found and excavated tracks in Wyoming, Utah and Arizona, and excavated a 30-ton slab from a coal mine in Colorado. Although he was not an academic research scientist, he did publish several articles in popular magazines, and he has become something of a folk hero in the annals of fossil footprint research.

Pasteur Ellenberger, Europe and Southern Africa (1970s until today). There are quite a few trackers actively doing research at the present time. One of the most interesting is Pasteur

23

Paul Ellenberger, a Frenchman who grew up in a missionary family in Lesotho, southern Africa. During his youth he traveled with his father all around the country trying to preserve a record of cave art made by Bushmen who, sadly, had been decimated by war and persecution. The Bushmen are said to be among the best trackers in the world, and among their cave paintings the young Ellenberger found drawings of three-toed dinosaur tracks and reconstructions of the bird-like animals that the Bushman thought had made the tracks. The tracks, it turns out, were very similar to those found by Hitchcock in New England, and were made by dinosaurs during the Triassic and Jurassic. Ellenberger also studied tracks from before and after the Age of Dinosaurs in his native France, where he made many significant new finds.

Father Giuseppe Leonardi, Europe and South America (1970s until today). Another priest who studies tracks is Father Giuseppe Leonardi, who originally came from Venice, Italy. His father was also a distinguished geologist who studied tracks, and he introduced Giuseppe to the subject at an early age. After studying theology and getting a doctorate in paleontology, Leonardi moved to Brazil where he worked for nearly 20 years. During this time he found countless tracksites on a continent where fossil footprints were little known and poorly studied. He eventually wrote a book on the subject reporting more than 100 sites, many of which he found and described himself

in dozens of other scientific papers. He also had many exciting and sometimes dangerous adventures in Brazil, Bolivia and Columbia — he was robbed by bandits at least twice.

Tom Brown Jr., New Jersey, USA (1970s until today). Unlike the five trackers mentioned previously, Tom Brown Jr. is a tracker of modern species, not extinct animals. As a young boy he learned tracking from an Apache Indian who was the grandfather of his childhood friend. "Grandfather," as they called him, had kept alive the type of expert tracking techniques for which the African Bushman are famous. These are more than just skills — they are a way of life. Besides allowing one to become an expert tracker, they teach an awareness of how to read nature and live in harmony with the natural environment. Some people call this "wilderness survival," but Brown describes his learning and experience as more of a spiritual communion with nature. Brown teaches tracking and has written several books on the subject. He often helps detectives find missing persons and fugitives on the run.

Joel Hardin, USA (1960s until today). Joel Hardin, a former police officer, is famous for finding more than 5,000 fugitives and lost persons in the last thirty years. "The International Society of Professional Trackers" regards him as one of the world's best trackers. Like Brown, he teaches classes on how to become a proficient tracker.

HOW FOSSIL TRACKS ARE PRESERVED

Many people are amazed that footprints are not immediately washed away and that they survive to become fossilized for us to see hundreds of millions of years later. The truth is that many footprints *were* washed away. But some survive. This can happen in at least two different ways. The first is the "cover up" explanation. The soft mud or sand in which tracks are made can be dried out by the sun and wind so that it is hard enough not to be destroyed by the next flood. The flood then washes a new layer of sediment into the area that covers and protects them. The second is the "direct deposit" explanation. Here the feet of animals stick through the soft layers of sediment near the surface and come to rest on layers underneath that are already buried. In this case there is no problem with the track getting washed away by the next flood, because the track is already safely buried and on its way to becoming fossilized.

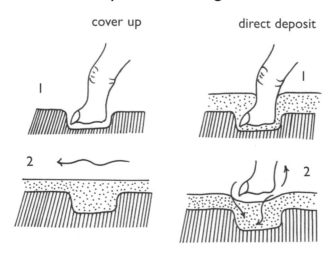

cover up   direct deposit

WHERE TO FIND TRACKS

Obviously it is easier to find tracks on soft ground than on hard ground. In many cases this means wet ground, but you can find tracks in the dry sand of deserts. Experience has taught paleontologists that most tracks are found along ancient shorelines. We also know that there are many types of shorelines, such as those along the banks of rivers, lakes, lagoons, and the sea. Some of these shoreline zones are narrow, but others are very wide. For example a coastal plain like the Gulf of Mexico is hundreds of miles wide, and it has many types of waterways and shorelines. In such environments one can find countless tracks.

We can therefore predict that fossil footprints will be found in sedimentary rock layers that represent ancient shorelines. It usually requires some geological training to find such layers, and it is not possible to collect tracks in many areas without a permit or permission. The track enthusiast may therefore wish to visit museums or known tracksites that are open to the public. It is usually possible to get photographs at such sites, and it may also be possible to buy replicas at museum shops. Several companies that make fossil replicas also make replicas of tracks. They usually select the best examples to carry in their catalogs.

A GUIDE TO IMPORTANT FOSSIL FOOTPRINTS

In the guide that follows some of the world's best known tracks, from those of *T. rex* to those of pterosaurs and our human ancestors, are illustrated and briefly described. Bear in mind the size of the track you are looking at by checking the description or scale. Some tracks, like those of brontosaurs, are almost the size of bath tubs, whereas those of small birds and mammals would fit easily in the palm of your hand. Some tracks have long Latin names, but the names can be interesting if we know what they mean. They may give us interesting clues to where the tracks came from, who found them or what they look like. This is all part of the detective science of tracking.

TRACKS OF INVERTEBRATES: ANIMALS WITHOUT BACKBONES

Trilobite trails

Trilobites were probably the first animals to leave a record of their footprints. They were marine creatures that became abundant in the Cambrian Period more than 500 million years

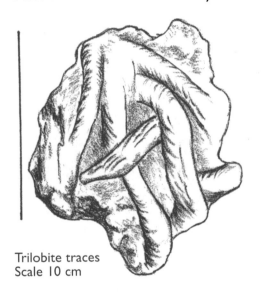

Trilobite traces
Scale 10 cm

ago. They belong to the group known as arthropods, which includes insects, centipedes, spiders and crustaceans (such as crabs and lobsters). In general appearance they looked a bit like wood lice or roly-polys, although some of them grew to be more than a foot in length. Others were tiny, no larger than a letter on this page.

Arthropods have been one of the most successful groups of animals in the entire history of life on Earth. This success began early and the Cambrian is known as the "Age of Trilobites." In addition to finding fossils of hundreds of species, we find abundant evidence of their activity in the form of trails known as **Cruziana** (pronounced Cruise-i-a-na), which are especially abundant in the Cambrian. This is a great name for their trails because it creates a picture of trilobites cruising the sea bed. Actually the name comes

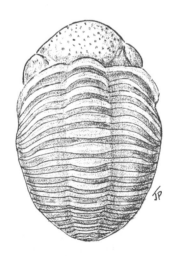

Track name: **Cruziana**
Animal: Trilobite

from the Spanish "cruz" meaning "cross," because the trilobites' many legs created a criss-cross pattern inside the burrow-like trail it ploughed in the sea bottom. Most *Cruziana* trails were made by medium- to large-sized trilobites, some of which had a dozen or more legs. With so many millions of feet in action, the Cambrian was the first true crossroads for tracks and trails.

Diplichnites: First trails on land

Millipedes and the first trails on land

There seems little doubt that the first animal to venture from sea to land was also an arthropod, perhaps even a close relative of a trilobite. Although we can't identify the exact species, it is certain that it was a multi-legged creature, for the trails are very similar to those made by modern millipedes. These trails have been given the name **Diplichnites** (meaning double row of traces). These trails appear as early as the Ordovician Period and suggest that both small and quite large arthropods had ventured onto land some 450 million years ago. By the Carboniferous Period some of these animals were huge, with trackways up to 18 inches wide. They have even been mistaken for the trails of amphibians! Again these animals may have looked like wood lice or the various large species of lice that still inhabit many shorelines today.

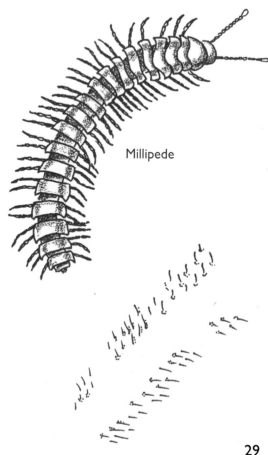

Millipede

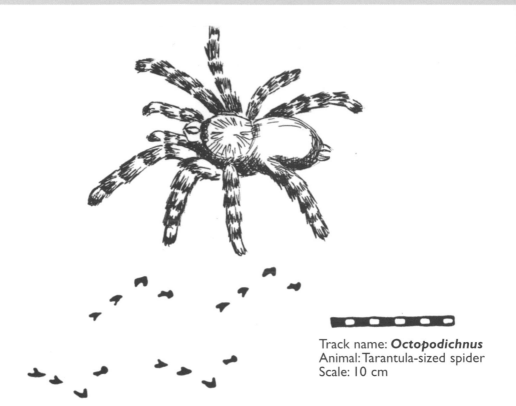

Track name: *Octopodichnus*
Animal: Tarantula-sized spider
Scale: 10 cm

Octopodichnus:
Spoor of the spider

As any biologist knows, spiders and their relatives, known as arachnids, have eight legs. It is not difficult to show that the trackways known as **Octopodichnus** (meaning eight-footed trace) were made by spiders. The most common examples come from ancient sand dune deposits in the western USA. These date from the Permian Period and are a little over 250 million years old. Many of the trackways suggest large tarantula-sized spiders with a leg span of as much as four inches.

Scorpion tracks

Also found alongside large spider trackways in the Permian sand dunes of the western USA are scorpion tracks named **Paleohelcura** (which literally means "ancient wound or scar"). These traces are virtually indistinguishable from those made by living scorpions.

The keen tracker can find many arthropod tracks in sandy deserts. They are particularly clear in the early morning when the sun's rays shine at a low angle. At such times one can find abundant evidence of the nocturnal activity of beetles, scorpions and many other creatures including small mammals.

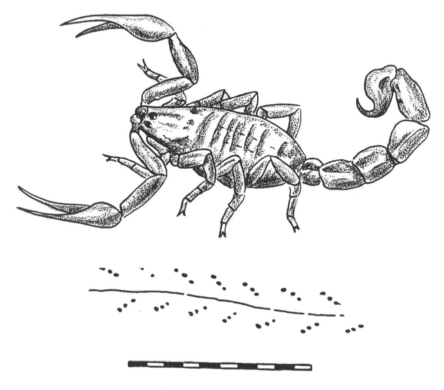

Track name: ***Paleohelcura***
Animal: Scorpion
Scale: 10 cm

Horseshoe crabs – dead in their tracks

An ancient and very large relative of the spider is the horseshoe crab. Rather different in appearance from living crabs, this primitive creature, whose ancestors date back to the Cambrian and Ordovician, has a huge horseshoe-shaped carapace (head) and a narrow sword-like tail. Indeed the name "sword tail" has been used to describe these creatures, which go by the scientific name *Limulus*.

Limulus and its ancestors have changed little during the last 400 million years and their tracks are similar wherever they are found. However their tracks, named **Kouphichnium**, can be confusing because their largest feet have five toes and can make tracks that look similar to those of small amphibians, reptiles or mammals. Indeed their tracks are often mis-interpreted. In one famous case, however, a Jurassic horseshoe crab was found dead in its tracks, leaving no doubt as to how the tracks were made.

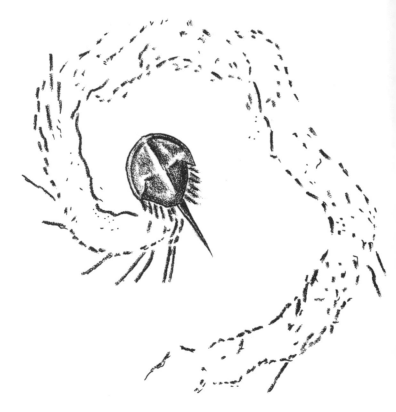

Track of *Limulus,*
the horseshoe crab

VERTEBRATE TRACES: ANIMALS WITH BACKBONES

Devonian beginnings:
the oldest vertebrate tracks
The earliest vertebrates were fish that were probably almost indistinguishable from marine worms when they first evolved in the Cambrian. However, fish that resemble modern species did not become common until the Devonian Period – also known as the Age of Fishes. When swimming in shallow water they sometimes made very regular sinuous S-shaped traces as their tails swished back and forth gently touching the sea or lake beds. Swimming trails like this are found in rocks of many different ages from the Devonian to the present; some have been named *Undichna*.

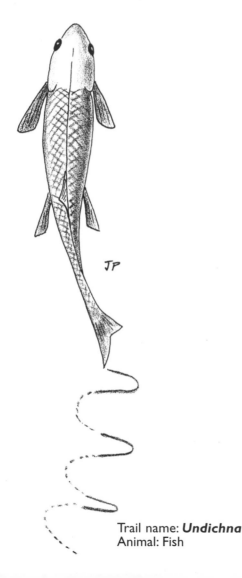

Trail name: *Undichna*
Animal: Fish

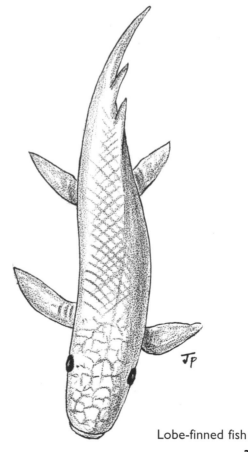

Lobe-finned fish

33

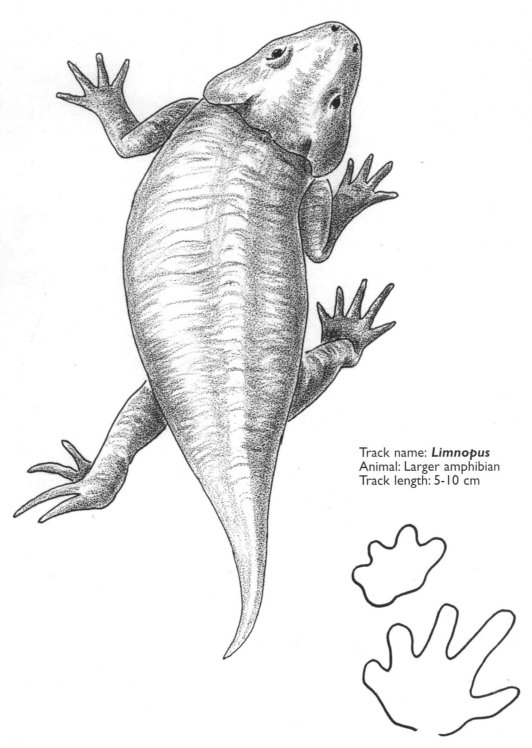

Track name: *Limnopus*
Animal: Larger amphibian
Track length: 5-10 cm

During the Devonian, however, a new type of fish developed with stout fleshy fins. This relative of the rare but famous Coelocanth belongs to a large, living fish tribe – the bony fish. Trackway evidence suggests that these forms, known as "lobe-finned fish" may initially have developed the habit of walking underwater. Some modern fish do this when stalking prey, and bottom walking is known among other aquatic forms like turtles and crocodiles.

The interesting question is, when did these fish first evolve into creatures that could walk on land like modern amphibians? We used to think that amphibians evolved from fish as a result of trying to walk on land – which caused them to evolve legs. We now realize that they may have learned to take their first walking steps under water. One thing is sure: the first signs of tracks of an amphibian-like species that probably resembled modern salamanders are found in Devonian rocks in Ireland, Australia and a few other places. This was the first step towards a permanent colonization of land. What follows in evolutionary history includes the evolution of reptiles (including dinosaurs), birds, mammals and eventually humans.

Carboniferous tracks

The Carboniferous was the Age of Amphibians and coal swamps, just as the Devonian was the Age of Fish. We therefore find many tracks that were made by amphibians of different sizes, as well as some that were probably made by early members of the reptile group. Few Carboniferous amphibian tracks are well known. However the minute tracks known as **Anthichnium** are worth mentioning since they give us a picture of a very small newt, or salamander-like creature, that was abundant throughout the coal swamps of the world. The trackway, known as **Limnopus,** provided evidence of much larger amphibians, several feet long.

We should bear in mind that there have been dozens, perhaps even hundreds, of names applied to tracks of Carboniferous vertebrates and invertebrates. To mention them all would double the size of this book. Nevertheless it is important to remember that the so called coal swamps were teeming with life, not just the few forms mentioned here.

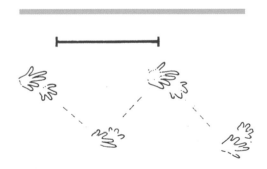

Anthichnium, a delicate little Carboniferous track made by a salamander-like creature. Scale 5 cm

PERMIAN TRACKS

The Permian Period is known as the Age of Reptiles, and should not be confused with the Mesozoic Age of Dinosaurs. In many regions it was a very dry period, and large areas of the continents were covered with sandy deserts. One might think that there would be few tracks found in deserts, but as we have seen it was a good habitat for spiders and scorpions. It seems that our mammal-like ancestors, the mammal-like reptiles, also liked deserts, as it is here that they seem to have evolved.

Dimetrodon tracks

Of all the reptiles known from before the Age of Dinosaurs, probably *Dimetrodon* is the most famous. This Permian-aged fin-backed creature belongs to the group known as mammal-like reptiles and, indeed, the Permian has also been called the Age of Mammal-like Reptiles. Its fin may have been used as a type of solar collector to help it warm up. The footprints of this animal are known from North America, Germany and France and have been named **Dimetropus**

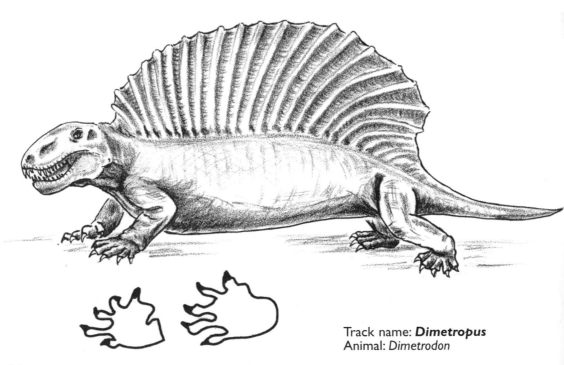

Track name: **Dimetropus**
Animal: *Dimetrodon*

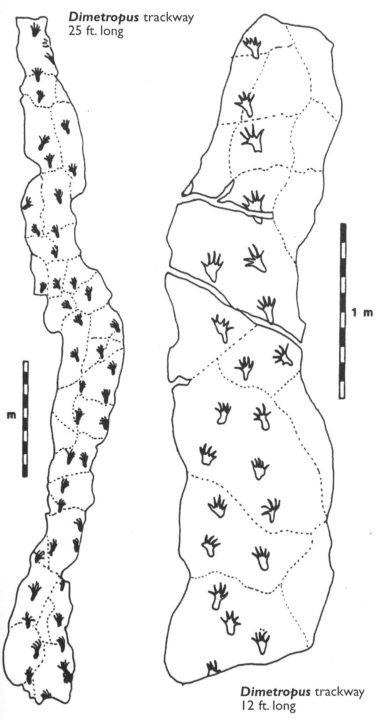

Dimetropus trackway
25 ft. long

1 m

Dimetropus trackway
12 ft. long

(meaning *Dimetrodon* tracks). Even though it was thought of as a sprawler, the trackway shows it walked in a fairly upright manner.

Chelichnus: **turtle-like tracks have another origin**
Another very interesting track type known from Permian rocks of North America and Europe is *Chelichnus* (meaning tur-tle or tortoise track). These were the first fossil footprints ever described, back in the 1820s, based on a discov-ery in Scotland. The Rev-erend, William Buckland, the first Professor of Geology at Oxford did experiments with his tortoise walking in pas-try dough to produce very similar tracks. How-ever, we now doubt that tortoises existed in the Permian, and we think the tracks were made by a type of mammal-like reptile. The rocks show that these tracks were made in ancient sand

Track name: **Chelichnus** & **Laoporus** in area of Grand Canyon
Animal: Mammal-like reptile
Track size: 3 cm long

dunes alongside tracks of spiders and scorpions. The footprints also show that these animals were capable of running up steep sand dune slopes. In the Grand Canyon region of Arizona these tracks have been given the name **Laoporus** which means "stone track."

Pachypes: **The Italian Bigfoot**
Pachypes (meaning "thick-foot") is one of the largest tracks known from the Permian. It was probably made by a strange animal known as a pareiasaur. These tracks are rare, and so far known mainly from the Italian Alps.

Track name: **Pachypes**
Animal: Pareiasaur
Track size: 25 cm long

Ichnotherium

Ichnotherium (meaning "beast trace") is one of the best-known Permian tracks from Europe. This beautiful specimen is from Germany. The tracks are about the size of a small human hand. The trackmaker was probably the animal known as *Diadectes*.

Ichnotherium: One of the most beautiful tracks known from the Permian of Germany.

Dromopus

Dromopus is a lizard-like track from the Permian of Germany. Usually about 3-4 cm long in the hind footprint, the tracks are almost indistinguishable from those of modern lizards. Though modern lizards did not exist at this time, many Permian animals had lizard-like feet.

Dromopus: A lizard-like track from Germany

TRIASSIC TRACKS

The Triassic is sometimes called the Age of Archosaurs. These animals were distinguished from mammal-like reptiles of the Permian by their ability to walk upright, either on all fours (as quadrupeds) or only on their hind limbs (as bipeds). The Archosaurs can be divided into three groups: the crocodiles, which did not walk upright and lived mostly in water; the extinct dinosaurs which did walk upright and lived on land; and the extinct airborne pterosaurs. We shall look at the tracks of all three of these groups in later sections.

Human hand

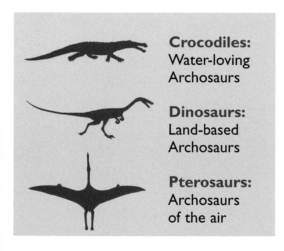

Crocodiles:
Water-loving
Archosaurs

Dinosaurs:
Land-based
Archosaurs

Pterosaurs:
Archosaurs
of the air

First, however, if we look at the tracks of the earliest archosaurs we may find the tracks of the first truly bipedal animals and the tracks of the immediate ancestors of the dinosaurs.

Chirotherium: **the hand animal**. Many tracks of archosaurs have an uncanny resemblance to the shape of the human hand. Such tracks, made by the animal's hind feet, caused much confusion when first discovered in Triassic rocks in Germany in the 1830s. Many wild theories were

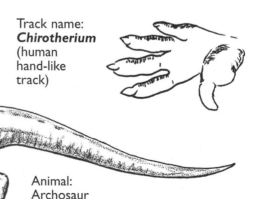

Track name:
Chirotherium
(human
hand-like
track)

Animal:
Archosaur

Drawing of tracks from 1850s publication

proposed suggesting that the tracks were made by various amphibians, apes, marsupials or bears. In fact it took a hundred years before paleontologists discovered enough archosaurs to understand what their feet and skeletons looked like. So the mystery of *Chirotherium,* the strange "hand animal," was finally solved.

There are many types of *Chirotherium* tracks, ranging from slender and delicate like a lady's hand to stout and large indicating bear-sized creatures. Some have even suggested that the differences are clues to different sexes of archosaurs.

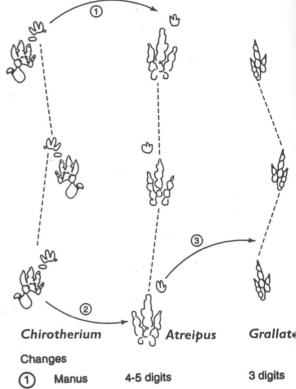

Chirotherium   *Atreipus*   *Grallat..*

Changes

		Chirotherium / Atreipus	*Grallator*
①	Manus	4-5 digits	3 digits
②	Pes	4-5 digits	3 digits
③		Quadrupedal	bipedal

Comparison of *Chirotherium, Atreipus,* and *Grallator* tracks shows change from quadrupedal to fully bipedal.

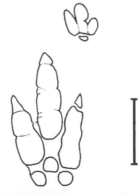

Atreipus tracks have a dinosaur-like hind foot, and a *Chirotherium*-like front foot. They may have been made by a dinosaur ancestor.
Scale 5 cm

Today, however, we know that these animals included many species that used their front limbs less and less for walking, leaving only very small front footprints in some cases, and none at all in others. One such example is the track type known as **Atreipus,** which has a three-toed hind foot like a dinosaur, and a tiny front foot like a *Chirotherium.*

Such tracks raise interesting questions about when we can first recognize true dinosaur tracks in the fossil record. We know that most dinosaurs walked upright and that many were bipedal. This new style of locomotion proved very success-ful and was also adopted by birds. True dinosaurs evolved about 220 million years ago in the Late Triassic, however tracks of bipedal animals that were probably very closely

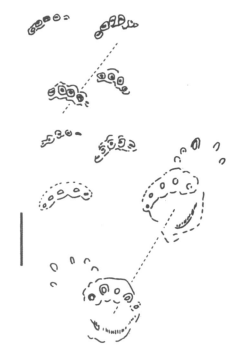

Track name: **Pentasauropus**
Scale: 50 cm

related to dinosaurs are known from the Middle Triassic, about 230 million years ago.

Therapsipus (far left) the track of a large, ox-sized mammal-like reptile from Arizona. Scale 50 cm

Dicynodontipus (left) the track of a small mammal-like reptile (Dicynodont). Scale 10 cm

***Pentasauropus*: the incredible five-toed track**

Mammal-like reptiles did not die out when the archosaurs became dominant in the Triassic. Proof of this comes from tracks as well as bones. The tracker priest Paul Ellenberger found large tracks of a mammal-like reptile in South Africa, which he named *Pentasauropus incrediblis*. This "incredible five-toed reptile" was the size of an ox or small hippopotamus, and appears to represent a large mammal-like reptile, such as *Placerius*.

Tracks made by similar creatures were found in Triassic rocks in Arizona and named ***Therapsipus*** (meaning track of a mammal-like reptile known as "therapsid"). Other smaller mammal-like reptile tracks from Europe have been attributed to dicynodonts (meaning "with two wolf-like canine teeth") and named ***Dicynodontipus***.

Track name: ***Pentasauropus***
Animal: *Placerius*
Track size: Up to 50 cm across

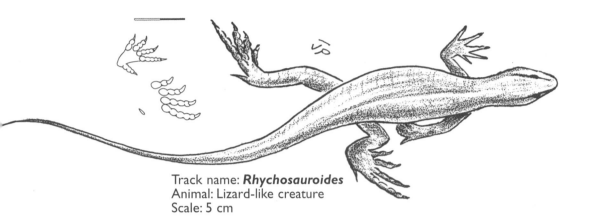

Track name: *Rhychosauroides*
Animal: Lizard-like creature
Scale: 5 cm

The first lizard tracks?

Along with archosaurs and mammal-like reptiles in Triassic rocks we find many tracks that are indistinguishable from those of modern lizards. Although there is some debate about whether true lizards existed in the Triassic, there were certainly lizard-like species that could only be distinguished from modern species by an expert. The smallest tracks are less than half an inch long, but others measure up to two inches or more. Their name (**Rhychosauroides**, meaning beaked reptile affinity) originates from the incorrect claim that they were made by beaked reptiles known as rhynchosaurs. They are very common in the Triassic, but rare in the Jurassic and Cretaceous.

Among reptiles, lizards are most closely related to snakes. Although we can find the sinuous tracks of modern snakes, especially in sandy deserts, there are no known examples of fossilized snake trails. The largest living lizard is the carnivorous varanid or monitor lizard known as the Komodo dragon. Its tracks, which can be 10-12 inches long, have been compared with the footprints of crocodiles. Komodo dragon-like tracks from the Triassic have been named **Apatopus.**

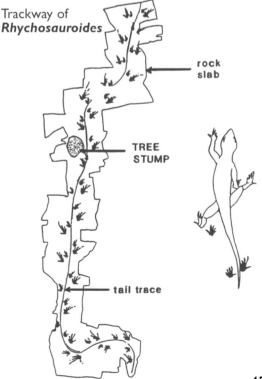

Trackway of *Rhychosauroides*

rock slab

TREE STUMP

tail trace

45

 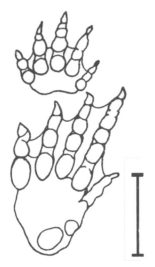

Rhynchosauroides (far left), the track of small- to medium-sized Triassic lizard-like species. Scale 2 cm

Apatopus (left), the track of a large varanid or monitor-like lizard that probably resembled a Komodo dragon. Scale 10 cm

Tracks of the first true mammals

The Late Triassic, which began about 220 million years ago, was a time of innovation. In addition to being the epoch during which true dinosaurs first evolved, it was also the time when true mammals first appeared. Their tracks show that they were all very small, mouse-sized animals, some of which walked and some of which hopped. Their tracks are so abundant in southern Africa that it has been suggested that there was an evolutionary population explosion at this time. Many names have been proposed for the south African tracks including **Eopentapodiscus** (meaning "early or dawn five-footed track"). Similar tracks are found in Colorado.

The first dinosaur tracks

As the Triassic drew to a close many different types of dinosaurs were evolving. Consequently, we find several distinctive dinosaur track types in Late Triassic and Early Jurassic rocks. The best known include the tracks of carnivorous dinosaurs and prosauropods, the latter being forerunners of the well-known brontosaurs. We also find the tracks of a group known as ornithopods (meaning "bird feet").

Oldest known mouse-sized mammal tracks, Late Triassic, Colorado. Scale 1 cm

EARLY JURASSIC TRACKS

Although dinosaurs evolved in the Late Triassic, they did not really become dominant until the Jurassic. At that time other groups such as the mammal-like reptiles, and other archosaurs that were not true dinosaurs, appear to have been on the decline. Many paleontologists suggest that the success of the dinosaurs had a lot to do with improved posture, which allowed them to stand upright. This improved the efficiency and speed of their locomotion, something that can be determined from their trackways. Examples of such trackways are well-known from the New England area, where they were studied by Edward Hitchcock. The best known types include:

Grallator: the stilt walker

This very slender-toed small footprint is found abundantly in Early Jurassic rocks in many areas. Many tracks are in the range of 3-6 inches long, but some can be as small as 1 to 2 inches in length. Typically these tracks show very clear rounded pads that mark the joints between the toe bones of the foot. The trackway is always very narrow, with a long step. This gives the impression that the animal moved very fast. To Hitchcock the name *Grallator* meant "one who walks on stilts" and implied a relationship to the bird family Grallidae. There are actually shorebirds named "stilts."

Track name: *Grallator*
Animal: Probably *Coelophysis*
Scale: 5 cm

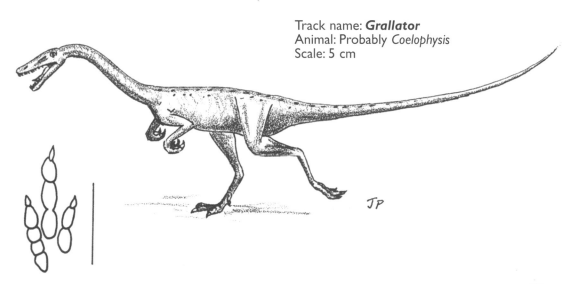

JP

When Edward Hitchcock first discovered such tracks in New England in the 1830s he called them **Ornithoichnites** meaning simply "bird tracks" or "stony bird tracks" as they were sometimes called. They were also referred to as the tracks of Noah's raven. We should also remember that dinosaurs were not known or named at this time, but the remains of giant prehistoric birds like the New Zealand Moa had just been discovered. It is no wonder that everyone thought they were bird tracks. We now know they were the tracks of small carnivorous dinosaurs known as theropods (e.g. *Coelophysis*). **Anchisauripus** is another name given to *Grallator*-like tracks.

In rare cases we find places where these theropods crouched down, leaving impressions of their ankles (the metatarsals) and pelvis. Some people think that they crouched down when they were stalking prey, but they may also just have rested in this position.

Eubrontes: **true thunder**
A much larger track of a carnivorous dinosaur, named **Eubrontes** by Hitchcock, was also, at first, taken for the track of a giant bird. Hence its name means "true thunder." Tracks of this animal are up to 15 inches long and suggest an animal on the order of six feet high at the hips and perhaps twenty feet long. The size of these footprints are very similar to those of a large Moa.

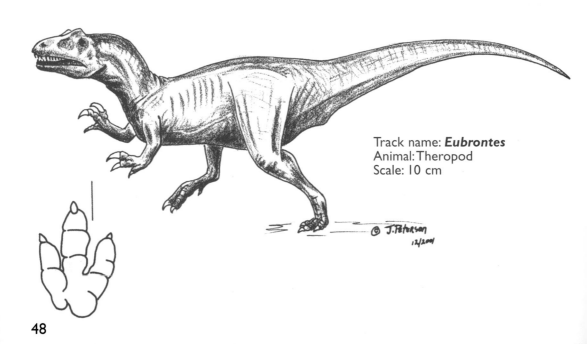

Track name: **Eubrontes**
Animal: Theropod
Scale: 10 cm

© J. Peterson
12/2001

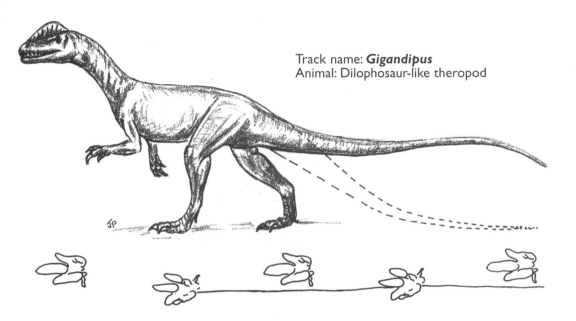

Track name: **Gigandipus**
Animal: Dilophosaur-like theropod

Gigandipus: the giant footprint

Gigandipus is the name given to theropod tracks very similar to *Eubrontes*, also found in Early Jurassic strata. However, they are different because they appear to have an extra digit impression. This is called the "hallux" and is common in many birds today. It is equivalent to the big toe (or digit I) on the inside of the foot. The *Gigandipus* trackmaker also appears to have dragged its tail, though evidence of dinosaur tail dragging is fairly rare.

Tracks similar to *Gigandipus* have been found in Jurassic rocks in Sichuan Province in China, where they have been called **Chonglongpus** (meaning track from the Chonglong area). They have a hallux impression and are sometimes associated with tail drag impres-

sions and crouching traces. Many other tracks are known from the Jurassic of China, and many have unfamiliar names. Because many of these are the same or similar to tracks we describe from other regions it is not necessary to mention them all. Lower Jurassic tracks from Iran have been named **Iranosauripus** – a rare example of a fossil footprint named after a country.

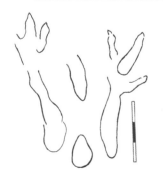

Crouching theropod dinosaur traces, Jurassic, Sichuan Province, China Scale 30 cm

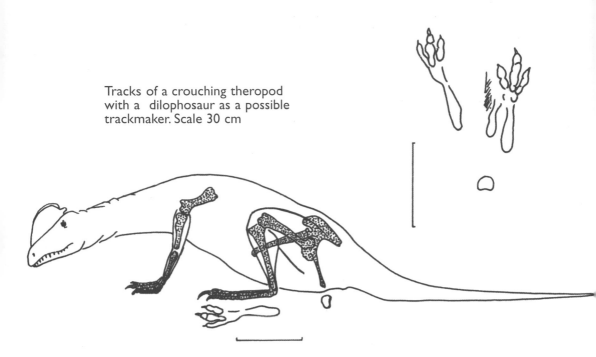

Tracks of a crouching theropod with a dilophosaur as a possible trackmaker. Scale 30 cm

Dilophosauripus and Kayentapus

Dilophosauripus is the name given to a track from Early Jurassic rocks near Tuba City, Arizona, where the dinosaur *Dilophosaurus* was found. *Dilophosaurus* is famous because of its distinctive nasal crests, and its starring role as a venom-spitting dinosaur in Jurassic Park. There is no actual evidence that it could spit venom. We do not even know definitively that it made *Dilophosauripus* tracks, though this is possible. The tracks are similar to other tracks from the area that have been named *Eubrontes* and *Kayentapus*.

   Kayentapus is another theropod track that is quite similar to *Eubrontes*. It was found in the Kayenta Formation of Arizona and named after the town of Kayenta in the Navajo Nation, near Monument Valley.

Otozoum: the giant animal

Imagine Edward Hitchcock's surprise when he discovered four-toed tracks that clearly could not be those of birds. Yet they also did not appear to be the tracks of anything resembling a modern species. All he could do was name them the tracks of a "giant animal," possibly some sort of reptile. We now think the trackmaker was probably a prosauropod, an ancestor to the true sauropods or brontosaurs.

   Tracks of the *Otozoum* type have been found in Late Triassic and Early

Jurassic rocks in Europe and South Africa, as well as in New England, and it appears they came in different sizes, from footprints only three or four inches long, like **Kalosauropus,** to footprints about two feet long, like **Pseudotetrasauropus** and **Tetrasauro-pus.** All three of these were named by Paul Ellenberger of South Africa, who also suggested that they were probably made by prosauropods. *Kalosauropus* which means "beautiful track," is similar to *Otozoum* and *Pseudotetrasauropus* only much smaller. *Tetrasauropus,* which simply means "four-footed rep-tile tracks," indicates a heavy fleshy foot that reminds us of brontosaur footprints.

Anomoepus: an odd track

At first sight the hind footprint named **Anomoepus** is very bird-like and also quite similar to *Grallator*. But on closer inspection of some trackways we find the traces of a small five-toed front footprint. Hitchcock, who named this track from New England, realized it could not be the track of a bird, and so suggested it might have been like a marsupial. In Hitchcock's day the strange primitive mammals of Aus-tralia, such as the pouched marsupials (including the kangaroo and koala bear, and the egg-laying duck-billed platypus), were still a puzzle to zoologists.

We now think that *Anomoepus* was made by an early representative of the bird-hipped ornithischian dinosaurs known as ornithopods. These are relat-ed to the early armored and plated dinosaurs, which became larger and more abundant after the Early Jurassic. Compare the front footprint of *Anomoepus* with that of a large armored ankylosaur and one can see the similarity. Some *Anomoepus* track-ways also show evidence of crouching down, leaving ankle (metatarsal), body and skin impressions.

JP

Track name: **Otozoum**
Animal: Prosauropod
Scale: 30 cm

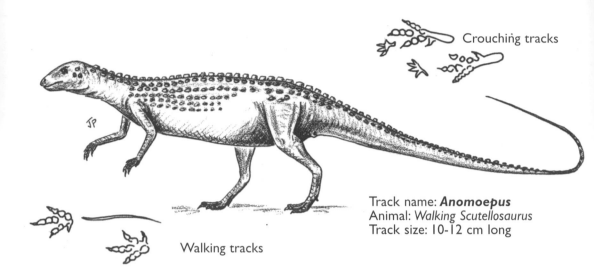

Crouching tracks

Track name: **Anomoepus**
Animal: *Walking Scutellosaurus*
Track size: 10-12 cm long

Walking tracks

There are many types of *Anomoepus*-like tracks at various sites around the world. One of the best areas outside New England is southern Africa. Here beautifully well-preserved tracks of this type have been named **Moyenisauripus** by the tracker Paul Ellenberger. The name means track from the Moyeni region.

Hopiichnus: in honor of the Hopi Tribe
Hopiichnus is another track from the Tuba City area of northeastern Arizona, named after the Hopi Tribe on whose lands the track was found. These tracks were made by a small bipedal dinosaur, probably an ornithopod. Many people now think that the track is the same as *Anomoepus*.

Batrachopus: spoor of a small crocodile?
Batrachopus is a distinctive small track type that was probably made by a crocodilian, or possibly a salamander-like amphibian. The name, first coined by Edward Hitchcock, refers to the archaic term "batrachian," essentially meaning frog or amphibian.

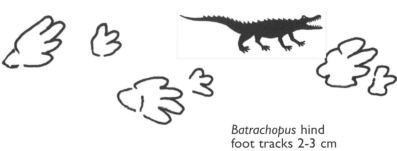

Batrachopus hind foot tracks 2-3 cm

Navahopus (left) tracks. Scale 10 cm

Brasilichnium (right), tracks may be the same as those named *Navahopus*, and were probably made by mammal-like reptiles. Scale 5 cm

Brasilichnium: the Brazilian track

Brasilichnium is a small footprint about the size of those made by domestic cats. They are found almost exclusively in Early Jurassic deposits that represent ancient sand dunes. They were first discovered by the tracker priest Giuseppe Leonardi at a town in Brazil where the track-bearing rock slabs were used for paving stones. Further study revealed that these tracks are almost always found going "up" the slopes of sand dunes. It seems that the routes they took to go "down" the sand dunes are not preserved. The same one-way, or uphill-only, pattern is noted for the Permian track *Chelichnus* in about 95% of cases.

It is no coincidence that the track looks like those of a small domestic cat or dog, because we now know that the tracks were made by some of the last of the mammal-like reptiles – known as therapsids. They are quite abundant in the western USA as well as in Brazil. Tracks from Arizona that resemble large *Brasilichnium* footprints have been named **Navahopus** (meaning tracks from the Navajo sandstone). These were found in the Navajo Nation of the four corners region. Some people think these tracks were made by a small prosauropod walking up a dune. Others think they were made by a mammal-like reptile about the size of a large dog.

MIDDLE JURASSIC TRACKS

Ameghinichnus: signs of a Jurassic gerbil

By the end of the Early Jurassic, as the mammal-like reptiles were going extinct, the true mammals had already been around for tens of millions of years. However, they remained small and inconspicuous and were still no larger than small rodents.

Tracks of a mouse-like animal. Scale 5 cm

These tracks are therefore hard to find. Rare tracks in a sand dune deposit of Middle Jurassic age reveal clear evidence of a hopping mammal no larger than a modern gerbil or desert kangaroo rat.

This beautifully preserved trackway was discovered in Argentina and named **Ameghinichnus** in honor of the paleontologist Carlos Ameghina. It is by far the clearest example of trackways that show our early rodent-like ancestors were capable of hopping. The track shape is similar to the early mammal track *Eopentapodiscus*. Hopping mouse tracks are also known from much younger desert deposits from the recent Age of Mammals.

Megalosauripus and Megalosauropus: on the trail of large theropods

The first dinosaur ever described, by

Track name: **Megalosauripus**
Animal: *Megalosaurus*
Scale: 30 cm

William Buckland in 1824, was *Megalosaurus,* a large carnivore (or theropod) found near Oxford, England, in Middle Jurassic strata. Can we find the tracks of this famous animal? There have been many reports of tracks named **Megalosauripus** (or some similar spelling) from Europe and other places as far away as Uzbekistan and Australia. Finally, however, tracks were found in rocks of the right age near Oxford. These suggest a large animal with short legs that walked with a rather irregular gait. This seems to fit *Megalosaurus* quite well. Tracks of this type from Upper Jurassic rocks in Portugal and Turkmenistan are up to 31 inches (77 cm) long, the largest from the Jurassic. At 85 cm, Cretaceous *Tyrannosaurus* tracks are the only theropod tracks that are bigger.

Megalosauripus trackways from Uzbekistan include the longest trackways ever measured. One, 311 meters or 1020 feet long, roughly equivalent to the height of the Eiffel Tower, holds the current world record.

Carmelopodus:
clue to a mystery trackmaker
Small dinosaur tracks can also be significant, especially if they are found in Middle Jurassic strata, which contains so few dinosaurs. **Carmelopodus** is the name given to a small theropod track found in the Carmel Formation near Dinosaur National Monument in Utah. We don't know which dinosaur made these tracks, but we know it had an unusually short heel on its outside toe. Similar tracks occur in strata in England. We can predict that one day we should find a trackmaker with feet to match.

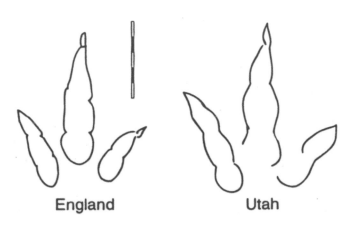

England   Utah

Carmelopodus has unusually short outside digits with three pads instead of four. This suggests that it kept its heel off the ground. Scale 5 cm

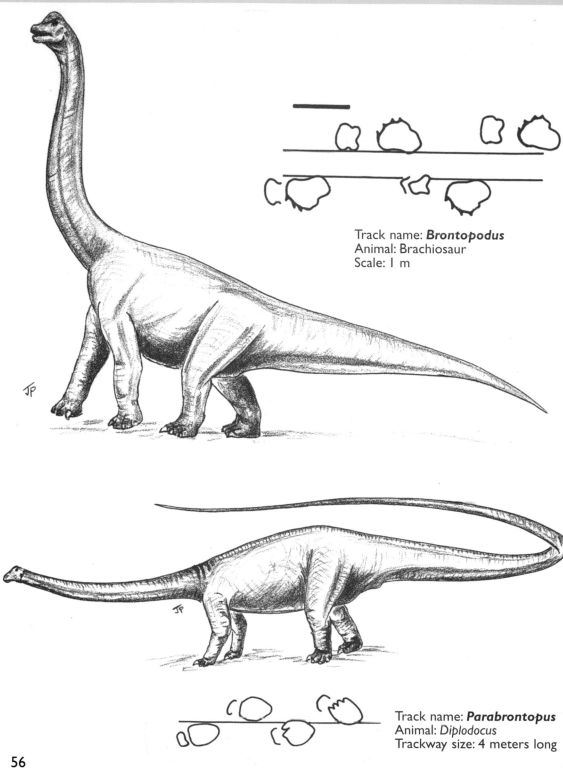

Track name: **Brontopodus**
Animal: Brachiosaur
Scale: 1 m

Track name: **Parabrontopus**
Animal: *Diplodocus*
Trackway size: 4 meters long

LATE JURASSIC TRACKS

The Late Jurassic epoch has been called the Golden Age of Brontosaurs. Tracks from this epoch are well known and include footprints of stegosaurs and pterosaurs as well as those of various brontosaurs.

Various theropod tracks

There are many theropod tracks known throughout the Jurassic and Cretaceous that all look very similar. One of the most distinctive is a track from China known as *Jialingpus* (named after the Jialing River in Sichuan province). Chinese tracks are often overlooked because western scientists cannot read about them in Chinese. *Jialingpus* is very well-preserved and in some cases has ankle (metatarsal) impressions.

Brontosaur tracks

Brontosaur or sauropod tracks include at least two types, those that are narrow gauge and those that are wide gauge – using an analogy with railway tracks. It appears that the narrow-gauge tracks which have been called ***Parabrontopodus*** (meaning like or "towards" ***Brontopodus***) were made by small, relatively light-weight forms like *Diplodocus* and occurred mostly in the Jurassic. By contrast *Brontopodus* (meaning brontosaur tracks) are wide gauge and occur in both the Jurassic and Cretaceous, and were probably made by brachiosaurs and titanosaurs. We also find that most narrow-gauge trackways have small front footprints and that wide-gauge trackways have large front footprints.

Brontosaur trackways are reported from many regions including Middle and Late Jurassic sites in Portugal and Colorado, and Cretaceous sites in Texas, China, Korea and Bolivia. A Middle Jurassic site near Fatima, Portugal has the world's two longest wide-gauge trackways at 142 and 147 meters.
(Late Jurassic continued on p. 78)

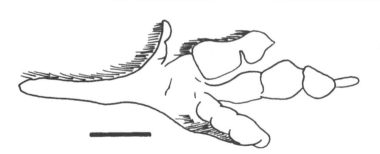

Jialingpus, a well-preserved theropod track with ankle impressions.
Scale 5 cm

Left: *Laoporus,* Permian mammal-like reptile tracks, Arizona.

Right: Similar tracks from the Late Triassic, Colorado.

Above left and right: *Grallator* tracks show long step from left to right foot with detail of left foot, Late Triassic, Colorado.

Below: Small mammal-like track, Late Triassic, Colorado.

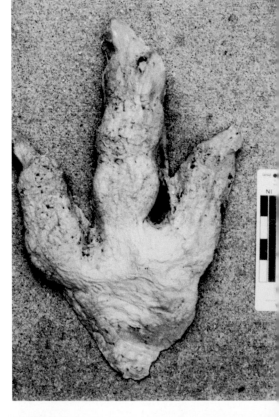

Upper left: *Grallator* tracks, Early Jurassic, New England.

Upper right: *Anomoepus* track, Early Jurassic, New England.

Lower right: *Eubrontes* track, Lower Jurassic, Utah.

Prosauropod tracks named *Otozoum*. **Clockwise from lower left:** Late Triassic track, Colorado. Lower Jurassic, New England; detail of skin impressions. Lower Jurassic trackway from Colorado.

Above: Lower Jurassic *Eubrontes*, Dinosaur Valley State Park, Connecticut.

Below: Small vertebrate trackway (possibly *Batrachopus*) from Lower Jurassic of New England. Note tail trace and raindrop marks.

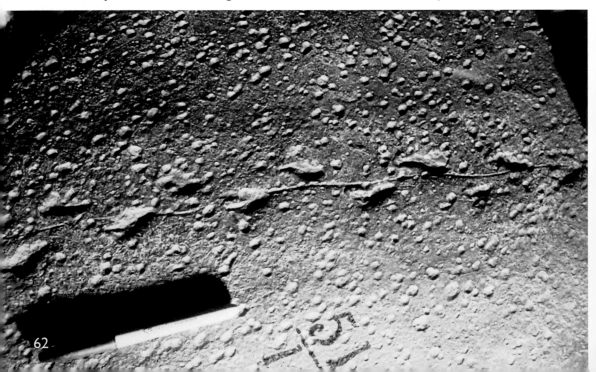

Left: *Therangospodus* theropod trackway, Upper Jurassic, Utah.
Right: Large theropod trackway (*Megalosauripus*) Upper Jurassic, Oklahoma.

Upper left and right: Upper Jurassic narrow-gauge sauropod trackway *Parabrontopodus* and replica of same for museum exhibit.

Lower left: Dinosaur track replicas for Museum exhibits.

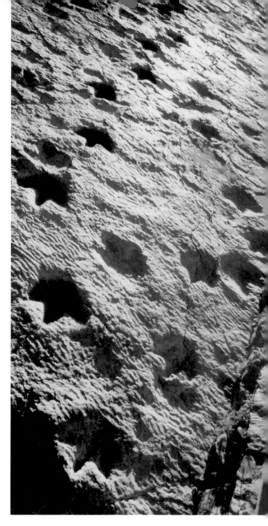

Upper left: Parallel ornithopod trackways, Lower Cretaceous, Gansu, China.

Upper right: Theropod trackways, Lower Cretaceous, Spain.

Lower left: Sauropod trackways, Lower Cretaceous, Gansu, China.

Night time shot of parallel sauropod trackways,
Late Jurassic, Colorado. Courtesy of Louis Psihoyos.

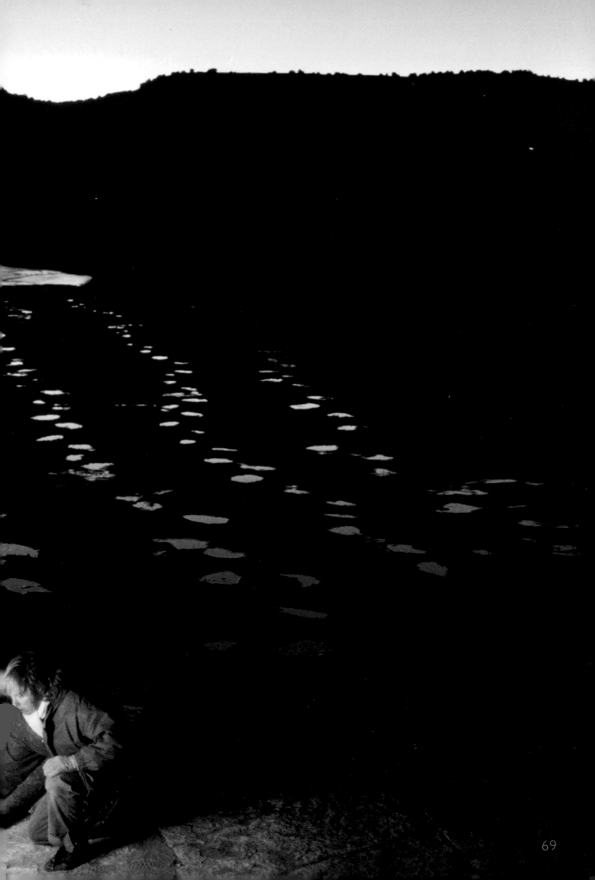

Left: Trackway of a turning theropod, Lower Cretaceous, Inner Mongolia, China.

Right: Trackway of a running theropod, Lower Cretaceous, Inner Mongolia, China.

Cretaceous tracks from Korea.

Upper left:
Sauropod

Upper right:
Ornithopod

Lower left:
Parallel ornithopod trackways

Cretaceous tracks on display to the public at Dinosaur Ridge, Colorado
Above: Summer view. **Below:** Filming with *National Geographic* in winter.

Small Mesozoic tracks

Upper left: Bird tracks beside dinosaur tracks, Cretaceous, Inner Mongolia, China.

Upper right: Cretaceous bird tracks with rain drop marks.

Lower left: Upper Jurassic pterosaur track, France.

Lower right: Cretaceous bird track, Canada.

73

Spectacular Upper Cretaceous sauropod trackways on a vertical wall, Bolivia.

Tracking dinosaurs on steep cliffs.

Left: Tracker priest Giuseppe Leonardi studies Cretaceous tracks at 10,000 feet in Bolivia.

Below: Theropod tracks on a steep face in the Cretaceous of Canada.

Ankylosaur trackway on ripple
marked surface, Cretaceous, Alberta.

Late Cretaceous bird and bird-like tracks.

Upper left: *Ignotornis* from Colorado

Upper right: *Saurexallopus* from Wyoming

Below: *Magnoavipes* from Colorado

Track name: **Stegopodus**
Animal: Stegosaur
Track size: 50 cm/pair

(Late Jurassic continued from p. 57)
Upper Jurassic sites in Portugal and Colorado have many trackways of both types, sometimes arranged in parallel sets that indicate herding behavior.

Cretaceous trackways from Texas were named *Brontopodus* following the suggestion of Roland T. Bird who found them in the 1930s. He also first proposed that they showed evidence of social behavior. The largest number of brontosaur trackways yet known comes from South Korea, and some of the longest and clearest trackways are found in Bolivia. Brontosaur hind foot tracks range in size from less than 20 to around 100 cm and are the largest known footprint of any animal.

Stegopodus: **and other hard-to-find stegosaur tracks**
Stegosaur tracks are rare. However one footprint, named **Stegopodus**, is a good match for a stegosaur front footprint. It was found in Upper Jurassic rocks in Utah. The complete trackway of a stegosaur ancestor is known from Lower Jurassic rocks in France. It is not really known why stegosaur tracks are so rare. Some people suggest it is because they liked dry areas where the ground was too hard to register footprints.

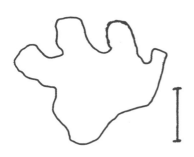

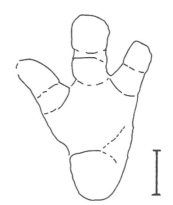

Stegopodus
(left), a probable
stegosaur front
footprint.
Scale 10 cm

A stegosaur-like
hind footprint
from France (right).
Scale 10 cm

Dinehichnus: in honor
of the Navajo people
Dinehichnus is another track in the
late Jurassic menagerie. It was named
in honor of the "Dineh," the Navajo
people of the southwestern United
States where it was found. It is considered the track of an early ornithopod,
probably a dryosaurid or a hypsilophodontid. The trackways suggest
evidence of gregarious behavior among
a group of turkey-sized dinosaurs. It
is a coincidence that another track
(*Hopiichnus*) named after a Native
American tribe, was also made by
an ornithopod.

Track name: ***Dinehichnus***
Animal: Hypsilophodontid
Track size: 15 cm long

Dinehichnus, an
ornithopod track
named in honor of
the Navajo people.
Scale 10 cm

Pterosaur tracks

The name **Pteraichnus** was given to
a probable pterosaur track found in
Late Jurassic rocks in Arizona in 1957.
These indicated a small seagull-sized
animal that walked on all fours leaving
an unusual front footprint where the
fingers on its wrist (part of its wing)
registered on the ground (see p. 15).

Paleontologists paid little attention
to this discovery, and in the 1980s
suggested that maybe the tracks had
been made by crocodiles. But, in the
1990s hundreds of *Pteraichnus* tracks
were discovered in Jurassic rocks in
Colorado, Utah, Oklahoma, Wyoming,
France and Spain. Pterosaurs became
very abundant in the Late Jurassic
and their bones are also found in
rocks of the same age.

Tracks that resemble *Pteraichnus*
are also found in the Cretaceous,
but in most cases they are much
larger. One from England is called
Purbeckopus because it comes
from a place called the Isle of
Purbeck. An even larger track,
Haenamichnus, from South
Korea is 30 cm long – the size
of a human foot – and has bird
tracks inside it. It could have
been made by an animal that
resembled *Quetzalcoatalus* –
the world's largest pterosaur.

Floating Pterosaur dragging feet

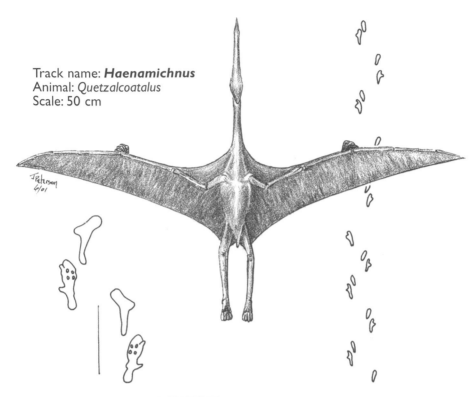

Track name: ***Haenamichnus***
Animal: *Quetzalcoatalus*
Scale: 50 cm

Recent discoveries reveal evidence that pterosaurs floated on the surface of the sea like modern seabirds. In shallow water they dragged their feet in the mud and sand to stop themselves from drifting or to stir up worms and other creatures that could provide a source of food. Some traces are scratch marks, others are toe and beak prod marks.

Pterosaur hind and front foot (top and bottom) shown next to a 5 cm lens cap for scale. Cretaceous of China

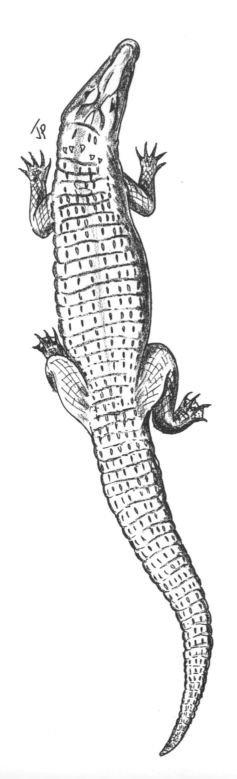

Track name: *Hatcherichnus*
Animal: Crocodile
Whole trace size: About 2 meters long

Track name: *Chelonium*
Animal: Giant sea turtle
Track size: About 15 cm

Hatcherichnus: a crocodile track

Fossil crocodile tracks are not common. Some represent regular walking, others indicate swimming. The tracks made while swimming consist of irregular toe scratch marks and tail traces. One distinctive track made in the Late Jurassic was named **Hatcherichnus**, after a famous dinosaur hunter named John Bell Hatcher who once found such a track. The tracks were found in a Uranium mine in Utah, and they show very clearly, the trace of a large powerful tail.

Chelonium: giant sea-turtle tracks

Tracks of giant marine turtles are known from Late Jurassic limestone in France. Some represent animals swimming in a shallow lagoon and occur as pairs of traces made by the tips of the flippers. Others look like trails where the animal walked on the bottom or in shallow water. These have been named **Chelonium** (meaning turtle tracks). This name is similar to *Chelichnus*, which is *not a turtle track*. A few tracks of small freshwater turtles are also known from the Jurassic and Cretaceous.

EARLY CRETACEOUS TRACKS

The Cretaceous is well known for its large bird-hipped dinosaurs (ornithischians). The best known include the duck-billed dinosaurs such as *Iguanodon* and *Hadrosaurus*, armored dinosaurs (ankylosaurs) and the horned dinosaurs like *Triceratops*. Lizard-hipped dinosaurs, including *Tyrannosaurus* and certain sauropods (titanosaurs) were also still quite abundant. At this time also we find quite a few tracks of waterbirds and pterosaurs, and even the occasional turtle, crocodile or frog.

Iguanodontipus: a link to Sherlock Holmes
Iguanodontipus is the name given to the tracks of *Iguanodon*, one of the first of the large duck-billed dinosaurs. This tribe of ornithopod dinosaurs was abundant in the Cretaceous. As the name ornithopod suggests they had three-toed bird-like feet. *Iguanodon* was one of the first dinosaurs ever discovered – in England around 1820. It was also one of the first dinosaurs correctly matched to its tracks. *Iguanodon* was common in England and Northern Europe in the Early Cretaceous.

Track name: **Iguanodontipus** (hind foot)
Animal: *Iguanodon*
Track size: 30 cm long

Paleontologists used to think that *Iguanodon* only walked on its hind limbs, leaving large, wide three-toed tracks. Tracks show that it sometimes walked on all fours, leaving small hoof-like front footprints. Some scientists suggest that young *Iguanodon* preferred to walk on their hind limbs. Sir Arthur Conan Doyle liked the *Iguanodon* tracks that were found near his home in Sussex, England, and included them in his famous story *The Lost World*.

Caririchnium: more tracks from Brazil

Caririchnium is the name given to dinosaur tracks from the Carir Basin in Brazil, which are very similar to *Iguanodon* footprints. They were also made by duck-billed ornithopods that walked on all fours. Similar tracks have been reported from Colorado and New Mexico, where they often show evidence of large herds that may have been migrating.

Amblydactylus: a Canadian big foot

Amblydactylus (meaning "wide toes") is the name given to a third type of Early Cretaceous duck-billed dinosaur track similar to *Iguanodontipus* and *Caririchnium*. These tracks are found in western Canada and also indicate animals that often walked on all fours and traveled in herds.

Trackway name: **Caririchnium**
Scale: 30 cm

Track name: **Amblydactylus** (hind foot)
Animal: Duck-billed dinosaur
Scale: 10 cm

Ankylosaur tracks

Armored dinosaurs known as ankylosaurs (referring to their "fused"
armor plates) were also abundant in
the Cretaceous, and their tracks are
known in North America, South America and Europe. The first tracks ever
discovered were named **Tetrapodosaurus**, meaning tracks of a four-
footed reptile. Another named
Metatetrapous is known from Germany. The tracks are generally large,
without a great difference in size
between back and front footprints.
This suggests an animal that was obli-
gated to walk on all fours. One trackway from Bolivia, however, suggests an
animal running at about 6-7 miles per
hour. Ankylosaur tracks resemble the
footprints of horned dinosaurs.

Bueckeburgichnus:
a theropod from Germany

Not many tracks of carnivorous
dinosaurs (theropods) from the Cretaceous have been given names. One

exception is **Bueckeburgichnus,** named after the town and geological strata of Bückeburg in Northern Germany. This trackmaker may have preyed on *Iguanodon,* which lived at the same time, and may even have been a threat to armored ankylosaurs.

Irenisauripus and Irenichnites: more Canadian tracks

Irenisauripus and **Irenichnites** are two types of theropod tracks found in the Lower Cretaceous of Western Canada. They represent medium-sized carnivores that may have been large enough to prey on the duck-billed dinosaurs that made *Amblydactylus* tracks.

Track name: **Tetrapodosaurus**
Animal: Ankylosaur
Size of hind tracks: 30 cm long

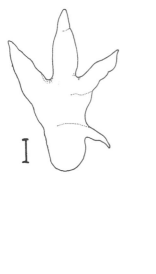

Bueckeburgichnus (far left), a theropod track from Germany. Scale 10 cm

Irenichnites (left), a theropod track from Canada. Scale 10 cm

Irenisauripus (right), a theropod track from Canada. Scale 10 cm

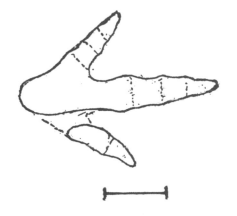

Ornithomimipus, a bird-mimic dinosaur. Tracks from Alberta. Scale 10 cm

Another Canadian track that seems to identify its trackmaker is **Ornithomimipus**, found in the late Cretaceous of Alberta and presumed to represent an ornithomimid or bird-mimic dinosaur.

Magnoavipes: **a big bird-like track**
Magnoavipes, meaning big bird foot, is the name given to large slender-toed footprints found in Middle Cretaceous rocks from Texas and Colorado. The trackmaker had feet about the size of a Goliath heron, Maribou stork, or large crane. Although the footprint is quite similar to that of a large bird, such as a heron, the trackway is very narrow with a long step, more like a dinosaur (see page 69).

Velociraptorichnus
As the name implies **Velociraptorichnus** is thought to be the track of a *Veloci-raptor*, the well-known sickle-clawed

raptor related to *Deinonychus* and *Utahraptor*. The tracks, which come from Sichuan province in China, are not sufficiently well preserved to be

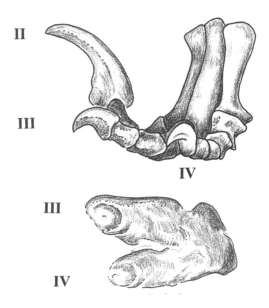

Track name: **Velociraptorichnus**
Animal: *Deinonychus* and *Utahraptor* (fossil bones)

certain that this interpretation is correct. The same is true of possible *Utahraptor* tracks from Utah. However, all raptors from this family (known as Dromeosaurids) probably only left two toe impressions as they walked, because the sickle claw was raised off the ground.

Other Chinese dinosaur tracks

We have avoided listing the names of many Chinese dinosaur tracks, because they may be the same as those already described from other sites. However, two examples of theropod tracks are worth mentioning: **Yunnanpus** (meaning track from Yunnan Province) and **Hunanpus**

(track from Hunan Province). Chinese provinces are as large as Canadian provinces or states in the USA, so these track names refer to important geographical areas, somewhat like the dinosaur names *Utahraptor* or *Albertosaurus*.

Cretaceous bird tracks

The Early Cretaceous was a time of rapid evolution among birds. At least a half dozen types have been named from Europe, Asia and North America. All appear to represent small waterbirds, shorebirds or waders that lived on lakeshores. Birds that lived in trees or walked in dry areas rarely left tracks that could be preserved.

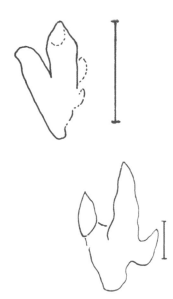

Velociraptorichnus (upper left), a purported *Velociraptor* track from China. Scale 10 cm

Hunanpus (right), a theropod track from China. Scale 10 cm

Illustration of a possible *Utahraptor* track, (lower left). Scale 10 cm

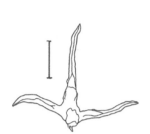

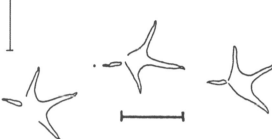

Archaeornithipus (above left), a large bird-like track from Spain. Scale 10 cm

Aquatilavipes (above center), small waterbird tracks from Canada, the USA and China. Scale 5 cm

Ignotornis (above right), this small bird track from Colorado was the first ever found from the Age of Dinosaurs. Scale 5 cm

Archaeornithipus
Archaeornithipus, meaning ancient bird track, is perhaps the oldest known bird track, found in 140 million-year-old rocks in Spain. They are about the size of turkey tracks, but much more slender. They are larger than most other Cretaceous bird tracks, and also show evidence of gregarious behavior.

Aquatilavipes
As the name suggests, **Aquatilavipes** is a "waterbird" track. Even an expert bird tracker would find it hard to distinguish this track from that of a modern shorebird such as a killdeer or a small sandpiper. This track was

Shore bird and track

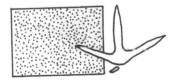

found in Western Canada in 110 million-year-old strata with the tracks of duck-billed and armored dinosaurs.

Ignotornis

Ignotornis, meaning bird track, was the first bird track ever found in rocks from the Age of Dinosaurs. This

Song bird and track

Tracks as clues to a bird's body shape

Song birds have long bodies, long tails, short necks, short legs and, generally, short beaks. Their tracks are long and narrow, matching their bodies and tails. Shorebirds show the opposite pattern. Their bodies, legs and tails are short, but their legs, necks and beaks are long. Their tracks are also short and wide, matching their bodies. Tracks can tell us, therefore, not only about the shape of the foot, but about the shape of the whole body.

hallux may be a clue to the length of the tail, the legs, and even the neck and bill of the bird (see box).

Koreanornis and Jindongornipes

Koreanornis is the name given to bird tracks from the Cretaceous of Korea that are probably about 100 million years old. They are very small and represent a species about the size of a small sandpiper.

The same strata contains tracks of a larger waterbird that has been named **Jindongornipes** (meaning "footprints from the Jindong strata"). Both of these bird tracks occur with the tracks of brontosaurs and ornithopod dinosaurs.

100 million-year-old track from Colorado had a prominent hallux equivalent to the big toe, but sticking out at the back of the footprint. This hallux is not seen in many shorebird tracks, but does occur in herons, storks and their relatives. The length of this rear toe or

Koreanornis, (above) the first
small shorebird track found
in Asia. Scale 5 cm

Jindongornipes, (below) the
first large waterbird track found
in Asia. Scale 5 cm

Uhangriichnus, (above)one of the
first two web-footed tracks found
in the Cretaceous. Scale 5 cm

Hwangsanipes, (below) one of the
first two web-footed tracks found
in the Cretaceous. Scale 5 cm

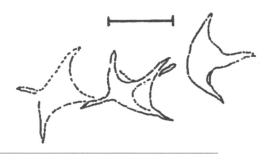

Uhangriichnus and Hwangsanipes
Two other track types have been named
from the Cretaceous of Korea. These
are **Uhangriichnus** (from strata known
as the Uhangri Formation) and
Hwangsanipes (named after the local
region). Both track types show evidence
of webbed feet, making them the oldest
tracks of web-footed birds in the world.
Korea seems to be one of the best
areas in the world for Cretaceous bird
footprints. Many are also known from
China, but few have been named.

Giant pterosaur tracks
Many Cretaceous pterosaur tracks are
much larger than those found in Jurassic
strata. For example, tracks from the Isle
of Purbeck in Southwest England, named
Purbeckopus, are 18 cm long, indicating
a foot larger than any known pterosaur
at that time.

   The English pterosaur tracks, however, are small in comparison with
Korean pterosaur tracks, named *Haenamichnus* (after Haenam, meaning
South Sea), which are more than 30 cm

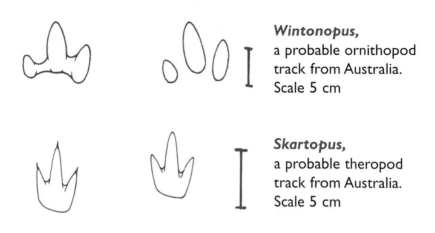

Wintonopus,
a probable ornithopod
track from Australia.
Scale 5 cm

Skartopus,
a probable theropod
track from Australia.
Scale 5 cm

long. These are the world's largest and must have been made by a species the size of *Quetzalcoatalus,* the world's biggest pterosaur (see p. 80-81).

A dinosaur stampede
One of the world's largest concentrations of dinosaur tracks is found in the middle Cretaceous Winton Formation of Australia. Tracks from this site have been named **Wintonopus** and **Skartopus**. *Wintonopus* is thought to be an ornithopod track, and is named after the rock formation in which it was found. *Skartopus,* from the Greek "skartes," meaning nimble, is considered to be a theropod track.

Brontosaur herding,
defense and trampling
We have already learned that the most famous brontosaur tracks are named **Brontopodus**. They were found by

Roland Bird in Texas in the late 1930s along the Paluxy river. The site is now open to visitors as Dinosaur Valley State Park. When Bird first discovered the site he reported twelve parallel trackways and was the first to suggest that brontosaurs traveled in herds. At this site the trackways were quite regularly spaced. He soon found another site with 23 parallel trackways that were much more closely crammed together with much overlapping.

Bird also noted the trackways of large carnivorous dinosaurs at the Paluxy site, and suggested that one of the carnivores had attacked one of the brontosaurs. A missing footprint in the carnivore trackway sequence caused him to speculate that the attacker had bitten the brontosaur's left hip and been lifted off the ground. This suggests a very dramatic scene: a one- or two-ton theropod attacking a thirty- or forty-ton brontosaur. But is this what really happened? If there were twelve giant brontosaurs moving along, could one theropod run in among them and attack just one, without causing any to swerve, change direction or stampede?

It has also been suggested that the 23 trackways at the other Texas site, known as Davenport Ranch, show evidence that the large animals walked on the outside of the herd to protect the

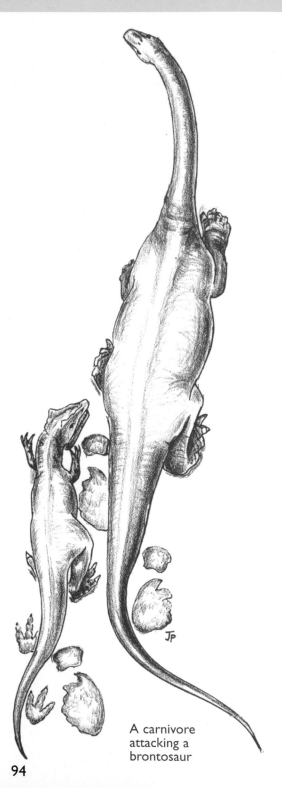

A carnivore attacking a brontosaur

Controversial trackways of a carnivore — supposedly attacking a brontosaur.

Pot-hole patterns reveal heavy dinosaur trampling in Cretaceous sediments near Clayton, New Mexico. Four-foot-wide board walk for scale.

small ones in the middle. This mode of travel is seen among African elephants today, but in general elephants are so large they do not have to worry about being attacked. The same was probably true of brontosaurs, so the idea that trackways show that parents were protective is controversial.

The pattern of trackways at Davenport Ranch is complicated, requiring good detective work to figure out which animals crossed the area first, and whether the small ones went first, in the middle or at the end. One thing is certain, the herd trampled up the soil as they passed through. Disturbance or perturbation of the soil and substrate by animals is called **bioturbation** and can be caused by all manner of creatures including worms, clams, burrowing moles and heavy-footed dinosaurs. Trampling by dinosaurs has also been called **dinoturbation**.

95

LATE CRETACEOUS TRACKS

The Late Cretaceous epoch is famous for duck-billed dinosaurs such as *Hadrosaurus*, horned dinosaurs such as *Triceratops,* and the king of the dinosaurs, *T. rex.* We have a pretty good idea what the footprints of most of these animals look like.

Hadrosaur tracks are much like *Iguanodon* tracks, though they are generally larger. Most hadrosaur tracks are known from North America, where they were particularly abundant. In western Canada (Alberta) and the western United States (Wyoming) we find hadrosaur tracks with skin impressions. In some states (Colorado, Utah and Wyoming) hadrosaur tracks

have been found in the roofs of coal mines, appearing upside down as natural sandstone casts, where the coal underneath has been mined out.

Some claims of hadrosaur tracks have proved quite wrong. For example tracks from Argentina (named **Hadrosaurichnus**) and Spain (named **Hadrosaurichnoides**) are not hadrosaur tracks at all. They appear to be tracks of theropod dinosaurs. Hadrosaurs and theropods had one thing in common – they were both mainly bipedal animals, though sometimes hadrosaurs went on all fours leaving small front footprints that look like those of a horse. But even when

Track name: **Tyrannosauripus**
Animal: *Tyrannosaurus*
Scale: 50 cm

we only have the tracks of the hind feet, hadrosaur tracks are generally much more "chunky" or fleshy and wide, whereas theropod tracks are narrow with skinnier toe impressions.

Tyrannosauripus

Tyrannosauripus (meaning *Tyrannosaurus* footprint) is the world's largest theropod track, measuring 34 inches long. This is exactly what one would expect from the king of the carnivores. It was found near Cimarron, New Mexico in strata that is the right age for *T. rex* skeletons. So far we have only found one track, so we cannot calculate the speed at which *T. rex* moved. Some estimates say at least 6 or 7 miles an hour, which is a pretty fast walk. It was probably too big to break the world record for a theropod, which is about 26 to 27 miles per hour.

Ceratopsipes

Ceratopsipes means footprint of a horned dinosaur (or ceratopsian). Tracks of this type were made by large quadrupedal dinosaurs in the latest Cretaceous times when the most famous of the horned dinosaurs, *Triceratops*, was common. In fact the strata containing these tracks in Colorado is called the *Triceratops* zone. There were lots of large horned dinosaurs like *Triceratops* around at this time and

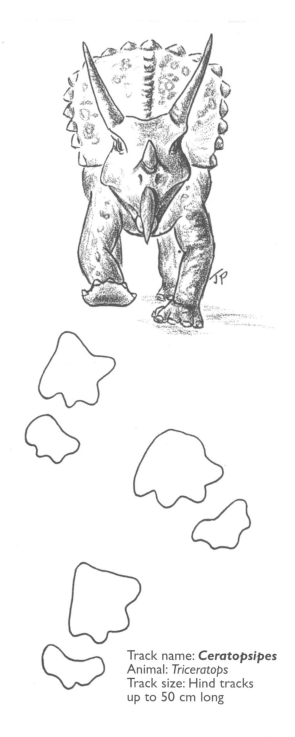

Track name: **Ceratopsipes**
Animal: *Triceratops*
Track size: Hind tracks up to 50 cm long

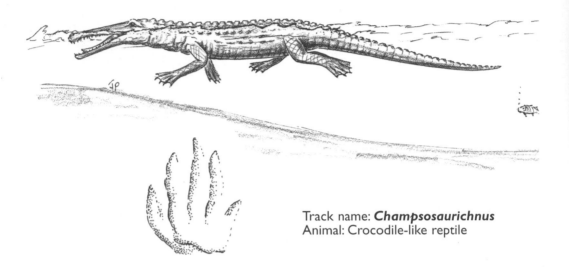

Track name: ***Champsosaurichnus***
Animal: Crocodile-like reptile

their footprints probably all looked somewhat similar.

The tracks of horned dinosaurs look a little like those of armored dinosaurs (see ***Tetrapodosaurus***). This is because they have four hind and five front toes. But there are also differences. The tracks of horned dinosaurs have rather blunt toes in comparison with the tracks of armored dinosaurs. They are also larger in most cases.

Champsosaurichnus
Champsosaurichnus means champsosaur tracks. Champsosaurs were groups of crocodile-like reptiles related to lizards. But like crocodiles and some lizards, they liked the water. For this reason their tracks are not common, probably because they did not spend much time walking on land. They have been found in Colorado, in the same strata as the tracks of horned dinosaurs and small lizards.

Lizard tracks from the Cretaceous of Colorado
Scale 5 cm

Saurexallopus (left), a large heron or stork-like track from Wyoming. Scale 10 cm

Xianxipus (right), a bird-like track from China. Scale 10 cm

Saurexallopus
Saurexallopus means "strange reptile track." This is a good name because we do not know what made this beautiful track.. It was probably made by a carnivorous dinosaur with a well-developed hind toe, as seen in many herons. This bird-like creature had a skinny foot with no flesh on the toes. Its tracks are found in at least two places in Wyoming. Similar heron-like tracks from China are known as

Xiangxipus (named after Xiangxi, the western part of Hunan Province).

Patagonichnus and Yacoriteichnus
Patagonichnus and **Yacoriteichnus** are the names given to two types of bird tracks from South America. *Patagonichnus* comes from Patagonia, and *Yacoriteichnus* comes from Argentina. They both resemble tracks of typical waterbirds.

Yacoriteichnus (left), a bird track from Argentina. Scale 5 cm

Patagonichus (right), a bird track from Patagonia. Scale 5 cm

Titanosaur tracks

Titanosaurs were a type of brontosaur (or sauropod) that was common in the Late Cretaceous, especially in South America. Titanosaurs had
large front feet and wide trackways.
Good examples of this type of trackway can be seen in Bolivia on a spectacular vertical limestone face near
the town of Sucre (see page 74).
In order to study these footprints
trackers had to use ropes to climb
down a 200 foot vertical rock face.
More tracks of this type are also
found in the mountains of northern
Spain.

The first frog tracks

In contrast to the track of a large
brontosaur, which is the size of a
small bath tub, we find the occasional
track of a very small animal such as a
frog. Only two sets of frog tracks are
known. The oldest comes from 70
million-year-old strata in Utah where
it is found close to bird tracks. Perhaps the birds were feeding on the
frogs. The second set, also found in
Utah in 40 million-year-old strata
from after the Age of Dinosaurs, is
also found with many bird tracks and
represents an animal hopping along
the shores of a lake.

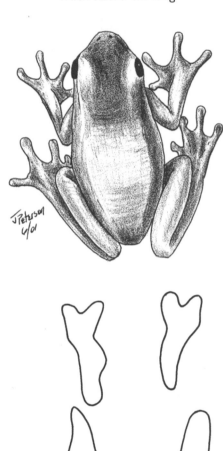

Frog and tracks
Track size: 3 cm long

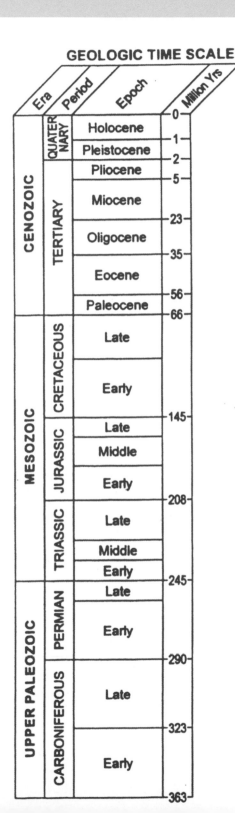

GEOLOGIC TIME SCALE

Era	Period	Epoch	Million Yrs
CENOZOIC	QUATERNARY	Holocene	0
		Pleistocene	1 — 2
	TERTIARY	Pliocene	5
		Miocene	23
		Oligocene	35
		Eocene	56
		Paleocene	66
MESOZOIC	CRETACEOUS	Late	
		Early	145
	JURASSIC	Late	
		Middle	
		Early	208
	TRIASSIC	Late	
		Middle	
		Early	245
UPPER PALEOZOIC	PERMIAN	Late	
		Early	290
	CARBONIFEROUS	Late	323
		Early	363

TERTIARY TRACKS

The Tertiary period belongs to the Cenozoic Era – or era of "recent life." In comparison with the Paleozoic Era (meaning "ancient life") dominated by fish, amphibians and early reptiles, and the Mesozoic Era (meaning "middle life") dominated by dinosaurs, pterosaurs and early birds, the Cenozoic is dominated by birds and mammals. Indeed it has been called the Age of Mammals. It is therefore not surprising that we find many mammal and bird tracks, and only a few footprints that represent other groups.

Mammal tracks
Among the main groups of mammals we have rodents, carnivores and ungulates (hoofed mammals), as well as rabbits and their relatives, insectivores, primates and proboscidieans (elephants and their relatives). Most of these left tracks that have been fossilized in Tertiary strata, or in the subsequent Quaternary Period, which corresponds closely with the recent Ice Age.

Tracking rare rodents and insectivores
Because rodents are generally small, their tracks are hard to find and so are rarely preserved in the fossil record. The same goes for tracks of small insectivores and rabbits. Nevertheless, 40 million-year-old tracks from the

101

Eocene of Texas suggest a small rodent, and a somewhat larger hedgehog-like insectivore (the latter named **Schyromorphipus** – meaning hedgehog-like tracks). In younger deposits in Colorado we find tracks that resemble those of modern deer mice hopping over sand dunes. On the Mediterranean island of Menorca probable tracks of a dormouse (**Hypnomys**) are reported from coastal sand dunes only one or two million years old.

Carnivore tracks

Tracks of the ancestors of modern carnivores such as dogs, cats, bears, raccoons, weasels, otters and the like have been found at a few sites in North America, Europe and elsewhere. A famous Russian paleontologist named Vialov tried to develop a system of suitable names for mammal tracks. He wanted all carnivore tracks to belong to a group called **Carnivoripedida**. Within this group he named the categories **Bestiopeda** (beast) and **Felipeda** (feline) for dog and cat tracks. He also had suitable names for the tracks of other mammals and birds.

Among the oldest carnivore tracks are 40 million-year-old examples from Wyoming, Oregon, Texas and France. The tracks from Wyoming are dog-like and may belong to a group of carnivores known as creodonts. Those from Oregon look much like the footprints of a modern domestic cat.

Front (left) and back (right) track of modern species
Tracks about 4 cm long

Track name: **Schyromorphipus**
Front foot (right) and back foot (left)
Animal: Hedgehog-like creature
Track size: About 4 cm long

Animal: Hopping dormouse
Track size: About 5 cm long

Tracks from Texas are quite varied and have been given names from A to Z. **Axicapes**, meaning "shear-like foot," and **Zanclonychopus,** meaning "sickle-clawed foot" suggest ferocious carnivores. Their tracks were the size of

large dogs or small bears. Little fox-like tracks have been named **Tetrastoibopus** ("four-padded foot") and **Falcatipes** ("curved sickle foot"), and a track named **Phacelopus** is attributed to a mustellid (weasel-mink family). The name **Mustellidichnium** exists for similar, but much younger, Ice Age tracks from Argentina. Anyone who can remember and pronounce these names deserves a prize, but even a non-paleontologist can see that they are the tracks of carnivores.

Hyena habits
Tracks from the Eocene of Europe have been named **Hyaenodontipus.** They were probably made by *Hyaenadon*, a hyena-like creature, but not a true hyena. True hyenas evolved after the Eocene. They are famous for leaving distinctive gnawing, chewing and break

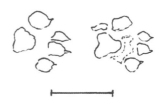

Axicapes (above), track of an Eocene age carnivore from Texas. Scale 5 cm

Tetrastoibopus (top right), track of an Eocene age carnivore from Texas. Scale 5 cm

Phacelopus (lower right), track of an Eocene age, weasel-like carnivore from Texas. Scale 5 cm

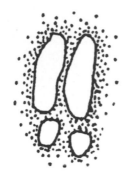

Pecoripeda, the name given to ancient cloven hoofed tracks.
Scale 10 cm

marks on bone and producing chalky white droppings (**coprolites**) full of bone residue. The famous English geologist William Buckland was the first to study the evidence of hyenas in Ice Age caves. In France their tracks are found in the same caves that contain footprints of our human ancestors.

On the trail of ancient cats
The oldest tracks of any member of the cat family may be those found in Alava Province in Spain. The tracks, from the Miocene Epoch (25-5 million years ago) are about the size of those of the modern European wildcat. They may have been made by a form known as *Pseudaelurus*. The site also has tracks of hyena- and mongoose-like species as well as those of a rabbit-like species.

Hoofed mammal tracks
The hoofed mammals are known as "ungulates." They fall into two distinct groups. The odd-toed varieties (perissodactyls) such as the horse and its rela-

Perissodactyls: odd toed – like the rhino and the horse.

Artiodactyls: even toed or cloven hoofed – like the deer.

Hind foot of a Miocene Epoch cat track 25-5 million years ago

Hind foot of Carnivore

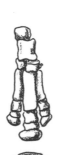

Rhino

Horse

Deer

Hind feet of Ungulates (hoofed animals)

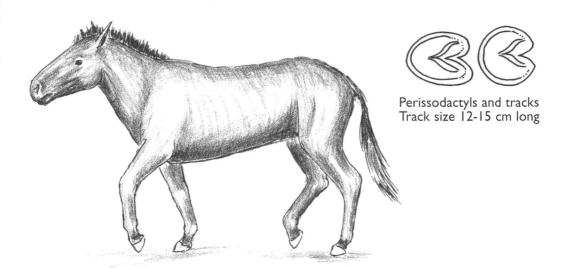

Perissodactyls and tracks
Track size 12-15 cm long

tives, which were more common in the Early Tertiary and the even-toed varieties (artiodactyls), including such forms as the deer, pigs, camels, sheep and cattle, which were more common in the Late Tertiary. The Russian, Vialov, suggested the names for tracks belonging to these groups. He also introduced the names **Hippipeda** for horse-like tracks, **Bovipedidae** for bovine tracks, and **Pecoripeda** for peccary or "pig-like" tracks.

Horse, tapir and rhino tracking

The horse, tapir and rhinoceros are closely related odd-toed ungulates. Tracks of horses, tapirs and their ancestors can be traced back to the Eocene Epoch, some 40 million years ago. At this time horses were tiny. The famous *Eohippus* (also known as *Hyracotherium*) was no bigger than a Scottish terrier. Moreover it had three toes, making its tracks much like those of one of its close relatives the tapir, whose tracks are common in

North America in the Eocene Epoch. Similar three-toed tracks are known from Europe, where they have been named **Paleotheripus** and **Lophiopus** suggesting that they were made by tapir-like animals known as *Paleotherium* and *Lophiodon*. Similar tracks are known from China and South America.

Tracks of 20-30 million-year-old tapirs and rhinos reported from

Tapir and tracks
Scale 30 cm

Nebraska encouraged a study that included experiments with animals from the Philadelphia zoo. The tapir proved uncooperative, but the rhino named "Peggy" made a good set for researchers to study. Rhino tracks of this age are found in France and named **Ronzotherichnus.** Younger rhino tracks (named **Dicerotinichnus**, after the relatively modern rhino *Diceros*), are known from Tanzania, Africa. The tracks of the relatively modern horse ancestor, *Hipparion*, are found nearby.

Cloven-hoof tracks
All the horned ungulates, especially the sheep and cattle (ruminants), and antlered animals of the deer family have cloven hooves. Usually only two large hooves touch the ground, but some-

Track names:
Ronzotherichnus
and **Dicerotinichnus**
Animal: Rhinoceros
Track size: 20-25 cm long

times the smaller dew claws leave impressions showing that the animal is actually four toed. Members of the camel family, which includes lamas and their relatives, are also even toed, as are pigs and their specialized relatives the hippos. There is little evidence of cloven-hoofed or even-toed ungulates (artiodactyls) leaving many tracks early in the Tertiary Period (65-35 million years ago). Later, however, from the Oligocene Epoch onwards, the tracks of cloven-hoofed ungulates become more and more abundant.

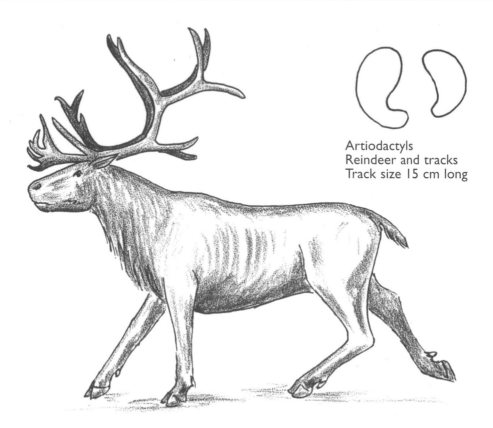

Artiodactyls
Reindeer and tracks
Track size 15 cm long

Possibly the oldest cloven-hoofed track is **Anoplotheripus** (perhaps made by the early ungulate *Anoplotherium*) from the Eocene of France. More typical is **Bifidipes** (meaning divided or cloven foot) from the Oligocene of France. Similar tracks are abundant in many Oligocene and Miocene deposits (35-5 million years old) from North America, especially in the high plains states of Nebraska and Wyoming where the ancestors of modern prairie ungulates such bison, deer and antelope have roamed for millions of years. Most of these tracks do not have technical names. Some were made by camels, which were common in North America until quite recent times. Their relatives the lamas, vicunas, guanacos and alpacas still live in South America.

Big Bird tracks

Diatryma is one of the most famous big birds of the Tertiary Period. It looked rather like a cross between an ostrich and a parrot. This large flightless bird of the Eocene Epoch was thought to prey on small mammals, but it may have been a harmless vegetarian that ate nuts and seeds. A track known from Washington state seems to fit the *Diatryma* foot quite well.

Diatryma and track
Scale 10 cm

resent larger wading birds such as herons, and others represent ducks and geese.

Very few fossil bird tracks represent songbirds, or other well-known groups such as raptors. This is not because these birds were rare, but because they normally perch off the ground, and so leave few tracks.

Bird tracks are common at a number of locations in North America, Europe and elsewhere. One of the most famous trackways is that of a 40 million-year-old (Eocene) web-footed bird from Utah. A clear trail of dabble marks along side the footprints shows where the bird used its bill to probe for food on the lake shore mudflat. In the same area we find frog tracks, and the footprints of at least three other species of shorebirds without webbed feet. The track has been named **Presbyornithiformipes** (meaning made by the fossil duck-like bird *Presbyornis*).

The paleontologist Vialov used the name **Avipeda** (meaning bird foot) for Tertiary tracks from Russia. Other names have been used for tracks from Europe: e.g., **Ludichardripodiscus** and **Pulchravipes** from the Eocene of France, and **Ardeipeda, Anatapeda, Charadriipeda** and **Gruipeda** from the Miocene of Romania. These last four names are not as difficult as they sound, especially for bird watchers, since they refer to well-known families:

Ducks, dabblers and other shorebirds

Bird tracks are just as common as mammal tracks, and sometimes more so. This is not surprising because today bird species are twice as numerous as mammals. Nearly all bird tracks found in the Tertiary Period represent shorebirds that probably resembled modern plovers and sandpipers. A few also repi.e., herons (Ardeidae), ducks and geese (Anatidae), shorebirds (Charadriformes) and rails and cranes (Gruiformes). They also follow the Russian scheme, and have been used for bird tracks from Texas. In Texas however another type (**Fuscinapeda**) is reported.

Tracks of the Lucy clan: *Australopithecus*
The oldest known tracks of an upright walking primate belong to our own family, known as hominids. These tracks were found by the famous Mary Leakey in Tanzania, East Africa, at a place called Laetoli. They are about

Heron and track
Scale: 20 cm

Ardeipeda, tracks of the heron family. Scale 10 cm

Gruipeda, tracks of the rail-crane family. Scale 10 cm

Anatapeda, tracks of the duck-goose family. Scale 5 cm

Charadriipeda, tracks of the shorebird family. Scale 5 cm

109

Track name: **Presbyornithiformipes**
Animal: Presbyornis
Track size: 8 cm long

3.0 million years old from the Pliocene epoch, and are associated with the footprints of thousands of rabbits, a Pliocene horse known as *Hipparion*, elephants, and various other mammals and birds.

The hominid tracks probably belonged to a member of the *Australopithecus* tribe, like the famous Lucy. At the Laetoli site there is evidence of two adults and a child walking together as a group – perhaps a small family. One of the adults stepped in the tracks of the other. The site is perhaps the most famous fossil footprint site in the world. You cannot see these tracks here because they have been buried for protection.

Australopithecus
Track size 25 cm long

ICE AGE TRACKS

The "Ice Age" refers to the Pleistocene Epoch of the Quaternary Period ranging from about 2.0 million to 12,000 years ago. For most people this epoch conjures up images of woolly mammoths, woolly rhinos and sabre-toothed cats, as depicted in famous paintings of Charles Knight or in Jean Auel's novels like *Clan of the Cave Bear* or *The Mammoth Hunters*. Many of these reconstructions show our human ancestors hunting these animals. Hunters from these stone age (Paleolithic) cultures would have been good trackers and we often find pictures of animal tracks on cave walls. There are also a few famous track sites, some inside caves and others outside.

Cave bear and track
Track size 30 cm long

Cave lion and cave bear tracks
Most cave bear tracks have been found in caves, along with many skeletons. This makes sense because cave bears hibernated and sometimes died underground. They also had a habit of scratching cave walls and even digging shallow pits called bear beds, nests or

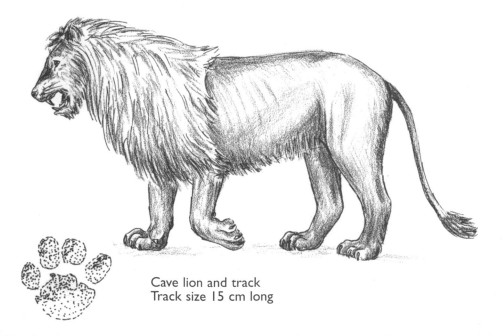

Cave lion and track
Track size 15 cm long

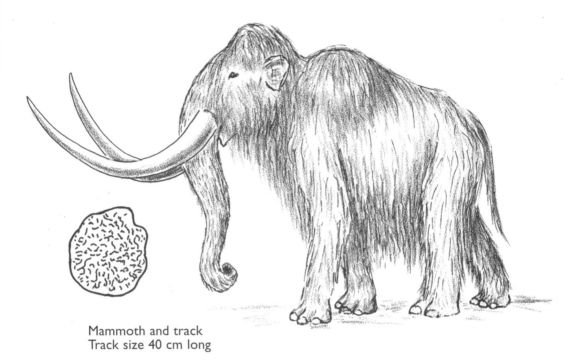

Mammoth and track
Track size 40 cm long

dens. They rubbed so often against cave walls that certain spots are polished and shiny.

Cave lion tracks and remains are rare in comparison with those of cave bears. One site near the Emscher River valley in Germany records a cave lion walking around in the open. There are also reindeer tracks at this site giving us the idea that the landscape was probably cold and bleak with glaciers nearby.

Mammoth and mastodon tracks

Mammoth and mastodon were common throughout different parts of Europe, Asia and North America during the Ice Age. However, despite being big animals, their tracks are rare. Could this be because they spent a lot of time walking on frozen ground? Tracks, however, are known from sites in Alaska and other parts of the United States. They have not been given scientific names, and in general appearance they are similar to those of modern elephants.

Giant sloth tracks

Tracks of a giant sloth that lived during the Ice Age were found in an unusual place – the compound of the Carson City Jail in Nevada. When first discovered in the 1880s they were thought to be the tracks of a large man wearing sandals of the type

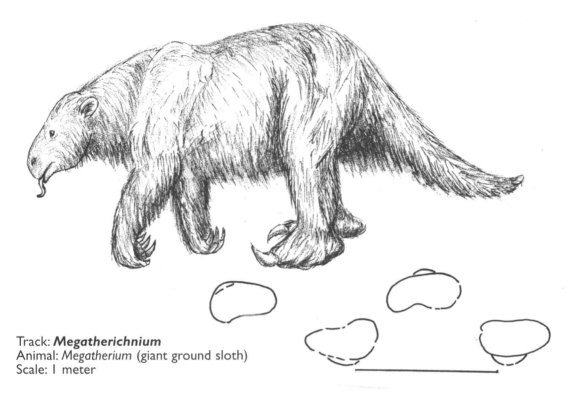

Track: **Megatherichnium**
Animal: *Megatherium* (giant ground sloth)
Scale: 1 meter

worn by Native Americas. Mark Twain wrote an amusing satire about this interpretation. The tracks were later interpreted as those of a giant ground sloth, possibly *Mylodon* or *Megatherium*, which grew up to 15 or 20 feet in length. Similar tracks from

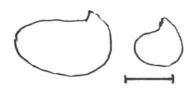

Neomegatherichnium, giant sloth tracks from Argentina. Scale 50 cm

Buenos Aires province in Argentina have been named **Megatherichnium** (meaning tracks of the *Megatherium*). Other similar sloth tracks from this region, in younger strata, have been named **Neomegatherichnium** (meaning "younger *Megatherium* tracks"). Tracks of the giant armadillo *Glyptodon* have also been reported from this area. These occur with tracks named **Lamaichnium** and **Pumaeichnium** obviously referring to lamas and pumas. **Tracks of *Homo erectus***

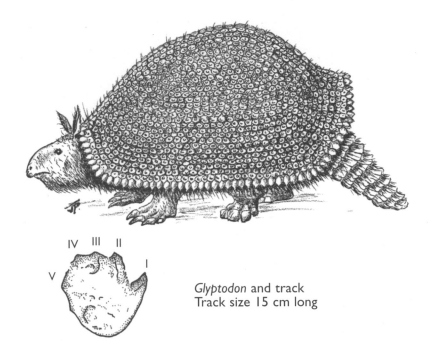

Glyptodon and track
Track size 15 cm long

Homo erectus (referring to erect posture) is considered the ancestor to our own species *Homo sapiens*. In comparison with *Australopithecus*, *Homo erectus* was much larger, and it is doubtful if one could easily distinguish its tracks from our own. A few tracks estimated at about 1.5 million years old have been found along the shores of Lake Turkana in Tanzania. This region of Africa is considered the cradle of humanity. The tracks are about 10 inches long and suggest an individual between about 5' 3" and 5' 11" tall. The site also contains the tracks of hippopotamus and shorebirds.

Neanderthal footprints

Anthropologists consider the Neanderthals, named after the Neander Valley, Germany, more similar to modern humans than any other extinct

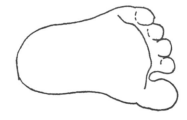

Neanderthal track
from an Italian cave.
30 cm long

species. The main difference appears to have been that they were quite stocky, heavy-set individuals based on their wide footprints. The example shown comes from a cave in Italy.

Ancient tracks of modern humans
Our species, *Homo sapiens*, is thought to have its origins some 50,000 years ago. Many of our earliest ancestors found their way into caves, where they left their footprints, tools and rock paintings. There are high concentrations of such evidence in some parts of Europe – especially France. At many of these sites we find human and ani-

mal footprints. Some footprints are clearly those of children, and at one site there is evidence that children were deliberately making tracks in a regular pattern as if playing a game. At another site there is evidence of an adult using some sort of walking stick. Most of these sites are at least 12,000 years old and represent human activity during the Ice Age.

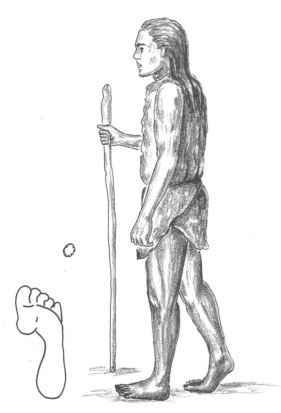

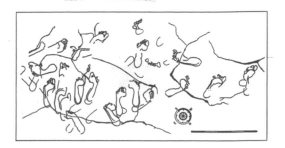

Left: Tracks of children playing a game
Scale: 50 cm
Above: Adult using walking stick

AFTER THE ICE AGE

The ice receded from the northern parts of Europe, Asia and North America 10,000-12,000 years ago and old Stone Age (Paleolithic) cultures gave way to those of the Middle and New Stone Age (Mesolithic and Neolithic). At various sites along the coastlines and muddy estuaries of England and Wales 4,000-6,000 year-old tracks have been reported. These are found in association with the tracks of deer, wild cattle, horses and shorebirds such as oystercatchers.

Moa and track
Track size 15-25 cm long

Tracks of recently extinct creatures

Many species have become extinct since humans evolved on Earth. Examples include mammoth, cave bear and cave lion. Tracks of these species may have been seen by other humans, thousands of years ago. Other tracks in this category are those of the Moa.

Moa is a term used for extinct flightless, ground-dwelling birds that lived in New Zealand. A dozen species are known from bones, and indicate creatures from kiwi to large ostrich size. At least two different track types are known. The large Moa goes by the name of *Dinornis*.

The Moa only went extinct very recently. The native Maori peoples of New Zealand drew pictures of them on rock walls and could remember hunting them just a few hundred years ago. Some Europeans claimed to have seen them less than 100 years ago. Another large bird the Takahe (scientific name *Notornis*) was reported as extinct up to the 1940s, even though people saw its tracks. Then a population was found alive and well in a remote forest area. What other creatures might be found in remote forests? Bigfoot perhaps?

Bigfoot tracks and other mysteries

Tracks of a giant primate – the bigfoot, or yeti, among other names – have been reported in many regions for hundreds of years, but especially in the forested mountain regions of central and east Asia and western North America. Some people have even claimed to have seen such animals. Is there really a giant primate wandering around these areas? Or perhaps, some say, such a creature existed until quite recently and is now extinct. Science has proven the existence of a giant ape named *Gigantopithecus* that lived in the bamboo forests of east Asia along side *Homo erectus* and the giant panda, now also extinct.

In recent years other large animals, such as new species of deer, have been found in these remote regions. Their tracks, like those of the Takahe, may be clues to animals that are not extinct. It is fun to think that we may discover new species and reveal new mysteries. Hidden cameras have been used to capture shots of rare animals in these remote Asian regions.

A history lesson

The Moa played an interesting role in the study of fossil footprints. When Edward Hitchcock first described bird-like dinosaur tracks from early Jurassic strata in New England, no dinosaurs were known with feet that would fit the tracks. So Hitchcock assumed that the tracks were those of giant birds, and called them *Ornithoichnites* (meaning bird tracks). When Moa skeletons were found in New Zealand at about the same time (1830s-1850s), Hitchcock was convinced that he was right. It was only later that Early Jurassic dinosaurs were discovered and described as the trackmakers.

Bigfoot and track
Track size 40 cm long

This story brings us almost to the end of our outline of fossil footprints. Many new tracks are found every year, and interpreted in different ways, not always correctly. For example, it is still hard to tell the difference between some bird and dinosaur tracks.

Detective work continues

Today's detectives deal with modern footprints, tire tracks and fingerprints. They make and store track casts that freeze evidence of crimes for future study. Scientific detectives also decipher our ancient history. For example at 2,000 year-old Roman sites in England, brick makers laid out clay tiles to dry, and during the night various animals, like weasels and badgers, walked over them leaving perfect tracks. Later, the Roman workers fired these tiles preserving them as rock-hard ceramic. Besides those at the tile factory, some may be found in the floors and roofs of Roman buildings. Imagine finding one on a roof tile. Did the animal walk on the roof, or through the tile factory?

Fossil footprints of the future

What would a visitor from another planet make of the tracks of NASA astronauts on the moon? Will these still be easy to find and study 1,000 or 10,000 years from now. What will future archeologists make of the tracks of film stars preserved in the cement of the sidewalk on Hollywood Boulevard? These are questions for future generations to answer. The detective work of science is never finished. Perhaps one day a paleontologist will find one of your footprints in cement or beside some lake shore. What stories will they reveal about your life?

Couple walking along lake shore

FURTHER READING

Leonardi, G. 1994. *Annotated Atlas of South American Tetrapod Footprints*. Ministry of Mines and Energy, Brasilia, Brazil, 247p.

Lockley, M. G. 1991. *Tracking Dinosaurs: A New Look at an Ancient World*, Cambridge University Press, 238p.

Lockley, M.G. 1999. *The Eternal Trail: A Tracker Looks at Evolution*. Persens Books, 334p.

Lockley, M. G., and Hunt, A. P. 1995. *Dinosaur Tracks and Other Fossil Footprints of the Western United States*, Columbia University Press, 338p.

Lockley, M. G. and Meyer, C. A. 2000. *Dinosaur Tracks and Other Fossil Footprints of Europe*. Columbia University Press, 323p.

Thulborn, R.A. 1990. *Dinosaur Tracks*. Chapman Hall, 410p.

INDEX

Track names in **bold italics**, as in figure captions and first appearance in text. Animal trackmaker genus names in *italics*. All other names and terms, including animal group names, in regular print.

WHERE TO SEE FOSSIL FOOTPRINTS

Fossil footprints may be seen at literally thousands of sites and museums around the world. The following is a list of a few of the more accessible sites. Consult literature and local professional paleontologists for further information.

AFRICA
Laetoli, Tanzania

ASIA
Samcheonpo, South Korea
Phu Faek, Thailand

AUSTRALIA
Broome, Western Australia
Lark Quarry, Queensland

EUROPE
Barkhausen, near Bad Essen, Germany
Carenque, Lisbon, Portugal
Cabo Espichel, Portugal
Cortedoux, Jura Canton, Switzerland
Dorchester Museum, England
Fatima, Portugal
La Rioja region, Spain
Lavini de Marco, Trento, Italy

Lommiswil, Switzerland
Munchehagen, near Hannover, Germany
Ribadesella, Asturias, Spain

NORTH AMERICA
Clayton Lake, New Mexico
Dinosaur Ridge, Morrison, Colorado
Dinosaur Valley State Park,
near Hartford, Connecticut
Dinosaur Valley State Park,
Glen Rose, Texas
Pratt Museum, Amherst College,
Massachusetts
Raymond Alf Museum,
Claremont, California
St. George, Utah
Tuba City, Arizona

SOUTH AMERICA
Araraquara, Sâo Paulo State, Brazil
Sousa, Paraiba State, Brazil
Sucre, Bolivia

ABOUT THE AUTHORS

Martin Lockley has spent twenty years studying fossil footprints around the world and is the author of several books and many scientific papers in this field. He teaches paleontology and related subjects at the University of Colorado at Denver.

Judy Peterson is an illustrator whose work has appeared in a number of paleontological publications.